Caring for Milwaukee

THE DAUGHTERS OF CHARITY AT ST. MARY'S HOSPITAL

by Brenda W. Quinn and Ellen D. Langill

❈

Photo Research by Marie C. O'Brien

Milwaukee Publishing Group
Milwaukee, Wisconsin

Right: *From 1861 to 1973 the Daughters of Charity cared for young girls at St. Rose Orphanage, located across the street from St. Mary's Hospital. The orphanage, as seen in this illustration, began as a two-story brick house, but was expanded in 1888 to a three-story structure—designed to house as many as 150 girls. The building was eventually razed to make room for Seton Tower, the Todd Wehr Diagnostic Center, and the new patient tower. Courtesy, St. Rose Residence*

Frontispiece: *Under the guidance of the Core Values of the Daughters of Charity, St. Mary's Hospital continues in its mission: The Charity of Christ urges us to Respect, Quality Service, Simplicity, Advocacy for the Poor, and Inventiveness to Infinity. The result has been and continues to be a hospital that creates an environment of healing, compassion, and excellence recognized throughout the community.*

Cover Illustration by Sister Theresa Marie Gresko, D.C.

All illustrations used throughout the book are provided courtesy of St. Mary's Hospital of Milwaukee unless otherwise indicated

Editor Karen Story
Photo Editor Doug O'Rourke
Editorial Assistant Kathy B. Peyser
Indexer Teri Greenberg
Designer Ellen Ifrah

MILWAUKEE PUBLISHING GROUP

David Turner, Publisher

Library of Congress Catalog Card Number: 98-67463
ISBN: 0-9650759-1-5

Contents

Foreword

For the past 150 years many Daughters of Charity, physicians, nurses, and support staff have ministered to the patients who came to St. Mary's to receive care. From the very beginning the sisters instilled a spirit throughout the institution by their approach to providing care. They believed that the patient should be treated as a whole person: in body, mind, and spirit. They also believed that all individuals should be treated with dignity and utmost

respect. Everyone who worked with the sisters was expected to treat patients and each other with these fundamental beliefs. The sisters knew that, although medical care delivery would change, the spirit in which that care was delivered would not.

I personally have had the privilege to experience that spirit at St. Mary's when I was accepted by the staff as their leader in 1989 and then later, when two of my family members were patients at St. Mary's. As the president and CEO of St. Mary's, I often received complimentary letters from patients and their families praising the professional, caring staff who supported them or a loved one through an illness. These letters rarely mentioned the latest in medical technology, but rather emphasized the kind, caring staff and their attitude. This is the spirit of St. Mary's!

As you read through this history, keep in mind the thread of this caring spirit. The values so inherent in the fiber of the organization are the spirit that has sustained St. Mary's through many changes in the past 150 years. This same spirit will be necessary to sustain it in the future.

Anniversaries give us all an opportunity to stop during our busy, active schedules and reflect on our history and those individuals who, with their spirit, developed the traditions of our organizations. The past has brought us to the present. We need to reflect on and appreciate the contributions of those who have gone before us, who paved the way for the present. This reflection can help us deal with today's challenges with courage and enthusiasm. I hope you enjoy reading this history of the ministry, not just of an organization or a business. Our good and gracious God has truly worked through so many wonderful people over the years. I hope you will join me in asking Him to continue to bless St. Mary's and its new partner, Columbia, as they join hands to share the future together. The future holds many new challenges for health care. Hopefully, we will sustain the spirit of serving everyone with dignity and respect. We will then know that the care that is given not always can cure, but can be an experience in healing of the body, mind, and spirit.

Sister Renée Rose, D.C.

President and CEO, 1989-1996

1946 -1948	St. Mary's celebrates centennial with solemn Mass and evening concert. History of Daughters of Charity in Milwaukee commissioned and published
1952	St. Mary's Hospital Guild founded by eight charter members
1957	Groundbreaking for new north wing (the Hill Building) takes place
1959	The Most Reverend William Cousins, archbishop of Milwaukee, officiates at opening of Hill Building in June. Burn Center opens in August
1961	St. Mary's enters into association with Mount Mary College
1963	Therapeutic section of radiology department begins operation with Cobalt 60 cancer therapy unit
1965	Cancer Diagnostic and Treatment Center opens
1969	School of Nursing graduates last class
1971	Cardiac program inaugurated at St. Mary's; first open-heart surgery performed
1972	Department of Respiratory Therapy implemented, as is telemetry for cardiac patients
1974	Family Practice Residency Program begins
1976	Seton Tower and Todd Wehr Diagnostic Center open. St. Mary's Hill Hospital moves into north wing
1980	St. Mary's Hospice program and cardiac rehabilitation program started
1981	Seton Children's School opens
1986	First long-term respiratory unit in Wisconsin established at St. Mary's, as are St. Mary's Sleep Wake Center and Senior Partners Program
1987	Project JULIE launched with NASA
1992	St. Mary's staff raises more than $10,000 for Mercy Hospital employees in Miami
1994	St. Mary's joins Horizon Healthcare network
1995	Sacred Heart Rehabilitation Hospital and St. Mary's merge; move to Lake Drive campus. St. Mary's Hill Hospital closes
1997	Arnold quintuplets born at St. Mary's
1998	Staff and volunteers celebrate St. Mary's 150th anniversary

A New Hospital in a New City

Foundations

I N 1848 THE CREATION of Wisconsin's first private hospital, St. Mary's Hospital of Milwaukee, filled a great need in serving the city's sick as its first organized health care institution.

The call to the Sisters of Charity of Maryland to come to Milwaukee and offer their assistance came from a settlement severely afflicted with disease and health problems during its first decade of growth.

It was indeed fortunate for Milwaukee that the Sisters of Charity answered this call for help, coming west to the Wisconsin frontier. Their leadership in founding St. Mary's Hospital and their dedication in nurturing it during the past 150 years have proven a blessing without bounds to the city and to the state.

In 1845 Milwaukee was a booming frontier port that both benefited and suffered from its growing tide of newcomers. The streets were unpaved and animals roamed freely, creating a multitude of health hazards. The animal excrement that filled the dirt streets, coupled with the open sewage dumped there, was ripe for the production of germs and the diseases they carried. While the new immigrants were welcomed for the wealth of talents and the labor pool they represented, they were also feared for the many new germs they brought. Without a central government until 1846 when the City of Milwaukee was officially chartered, the three river settlements that made up Milwaukee (Juneautown, Kilbourntown, and Walker's Point) were unable to deal with the many diseases and rising death rate among the population.

Bishop John Martin Henni

In trying to address these problems, private individuals began a campaign to "clean up the city," which included getting pigs and cattle off the streets, beginning to pave the roads, controlling the sewage, and bringing some form of health care and health awareness to the citizens. One of these civic leaders, Bishop John Martin Henni, took the lead in meeting the needs of the city's sick and poor and in creating St. Mary's Hospital, the first such institution in the city and in the state of Wisconsin in 1848. Originally from Switzerland and a recent immigrant to Milwaukee, Henni understood both the homelessness of many of the new arrivals and their need for a sense of community.

He and fellow priest Martin Kundig, also from Switzerland, organized both German and Irish Catholics in the city into strong parishes, the churches of St. Peter's, St. Mary's, and St. John's. Henni came to Milwaukee in 1843 from Cincinnati where he had edited the first German Catholic newspaper in America. In Milwaukee, as the newly appointed bishop, he sought to bring Catholics from many nationalities together through parades and festivals, and also to lead them in providing schools and social services to the needy of all religions among the city's growing population. One of the hallmarks of the infirmary and hospital he founded with the Sisters of Charity in Milwaukee was an absolute commitment to help the sick of all religions, all nationalities, and all races.

With the increasing incidence of malaria, smallpox, typhus, and cholera among the city's population, Henni decided to take action to provide health care through the organized church. From his roots in Europe, he was aware of the traditions of the French Daughters of Charity, as well as their descendants, the Sisters of Charity from Emmitsburg, Maryland. His emphasis on schooling and on care for the sick dovetailed perfectly with the mission and the history of the Sisters of Charity, about whom he had written in his newspaper in Cincinnati and who had a strong presence in both Cincinnati and in nearby Evansville, Indiana.

In assessing the situation in Milwaukee, Bishop Henni realized that the Sisters of Charity were the one group that could provide both the parish schooling and the badly needed nursing skills for the city's poor. His call for help reached to their order in Emmitsburg, Maryland, near Baltimore, which had its roots in the pattern of Catholic service by women in seventeenth-century France. Milwaukee received the caring vigilance and professional expertise in health care of these Sisters of Charity when they arrived in the city to heed Henni's call, a vigilance and dedication that dated back to Europe more than two centuries earlier.

St. Vincent de Paul, St. Louise de Marillac, and the Daughters of Charity

The seeds of St. Mary's Hospital of Milwaukee were first sown in seventeenth-century France, where Catholic leaders originated the concept of ministering to bodies as well as souls.

The priest who later became St. Vincent de Paul and a powerful and dedicated Catholic lay woman, Louise de Marillac, founded the Daughters of Charity (also called the Sisters of Charity) to provide for the poor of Paris in 1633.

In the early 1600s Paris bore a strong resemblance to Milwaukee in the mid-1800s, lacking running water, a sewer system, or electricity. There were no social services, and only the wealthy could afford any medical care. Physicians at that time operated without a license or any professional oversight, leading to gross ineptness among many. It was said that "keeping a doctor away" was the best chance to recover from an illness, since many doctors were charlatans who used unorthodox practices or concocted medicines. Wisconsin, in the early 1800s, also had few standards and no required license to practice medicine.

Vincent de Paul was born in 1580 in Pouy, a town in southern France. The third of six children of hard-working farmers, he was sent by his father to study for the priesthood, a vocation that would enable him to support his family. He attended a church school and proved to be such a dedicated scholar that he was able to further his education at the University of Paris. Graduating at age 20, he was ordained in 1600 and took to the road to learn more about the world.

While traveling through Europe, Father Vincent was captured by Barbary pirates and sold into slavery.

Facing: St. Peter's Church, located on the northwest corner of East State and North Jackson streets, became the city's first parish in 1839. Upon their arrival, the sisters took over teaching of the girl's school in the basement of the church, thereby assisting in launching Milwaukee's Catholic parochial school system. The original cathedral was restored and now stands in Eagle, Wisconsin. Courtesy, Archives of the Archdiocese of Milwaukee

Bishop John Martin Henni was responsible for the Sisters (now the Daughters) of Charity coming to Milwaukee in 1846. He was ordained in Cincinnati on April 6, 1822, and it was there that he became acquainted with the order of the Sisters of Charity. He was appointed bishop of Milwaukee in 1843. Two years later he wrote to the motherhouse in Emmitsburg, Maryland, asking for two or three sisters to come to Milwaukee to teach school and to start a hospital. Courtesy, Milwaukee County Historical Society

The Daughters of Charity in America attribute their origins to Elizabeth Ann Seton. The daughter of a physician, the 19-year-old Elizabeth Ann Bayley married William Seton—only to become a widow a few years later. In 1808 she opened a small school in Baltimore, Maryland, sparking the beginning of the Catholic school system in the United States. After taking vows of poverty, chastity, and obedience, she was given the title Mother Seton and began sisterhood with her followers as the Sisters of Charity of St. Joseph. In 1850, nearly 30 years after her death, the sisters became unified with the Daughters of Charity. Elizabeth Ann Seton was beatified in 1963 and canonized in 1975.

He escaped, and ultimately continued his studies. His abilities and holiness were recognized and he was valued for his brilliance and for his dedication to human improvement. He eventually became chaplain to Queen Margaret of Valois in Paris. He was respected by royalty and well known among the nobility, but his heart was with the poor.

Soon he found that he could no longer remain a servant to the wealthy, while unable to bring some relief to the many starving and sick people he witnessed daily in the streets of Paris.

In 1625 he founded the Vincentians, an order of men devoted to missionary work among the peasantry. Perceiving the special need of many of the poor for physical care, he worked with another future saint, Louise de Marillac, to organize the Confraternities of Charity, wealthy women who performed works of charity at the parish level. Louise de Marillac was born in 1591, the illegitimate daughter of a nobleman. She was convent educated, and married in 1613. After the death of her husband in 1625, she met Father Vincent de Paul and began to help him with his work.

Together they conceived of the idea of establishing a service order of Catholic women and girls—to be called the Daughters of Charity—that would train them in the care of the sick and utilize their skills to minister to the many poor people who had no health services at all. They had witnessed the food donations of the wealthy often going to waste because of the lack of an organized distribution network, just as they witnessed a need for the actual "hands-on" service in caring for the sick and needy. They believed that they could train peasant girls, many of whom had heard of St. Vincent and asked to work with him, for this service.

In providing training to women and adolescent girls, the order also performed the benefit of giving them some education (a rare commodity for women in the 1600s), religious training, and a purpose in life. Education in the care of the sick, and later in formal nurses' training, became a hallmark of the order, allowing great opportunities for betterment among disadvantaged girls, and utilizing their gifts to aid the needy.

Louise and Vincent established the first training center in 1633 in Louise's own home in Paris. The idea was not to form a religious community but rather a group of pious women living together. It was not until 1640 that some of the women requested to take simple private vows. In time this was formalized, with the civil authorities recognizing the community in 1658 followed by the Catholic Church in 1669.

To emphasize their call to worldly service, Louise and Vincent insisted that the sisters not dress in distinguishing habits, that they live in a motherhouse, rather than cloistered in a convent retreat, and that their leader be called a "sister servant," rather than a superior. They reached out to embrace the world and tried to solve its problems by active ministry of word and deed. As the group grew in numbers during its first few years, the sisters were able to take care of people in private homes, on the streets, and in a city hospital, the "Hotel Dieu" in Paris.

This "Mansion of God," as it was known, became so over-crowded that the nurses often had to put as many as three or four people in each bed. As in most hospitals of the seventeenth through early nineteenth centuries, up to one-half of the patients routinely died. Doctors and hospitals simply could not cure most diseases at that time, and only a healthy constitution, good food, and rest might allow for healing. These early hospitals tried to provide these three ingredients, at a minimum, as did the hospitals in frontier Milwaukee in the 1840s and 1850s.

In 1644 Louise devised a system for separating the operations of feeding the poor, child care, nursing, and education. In doing so, she pointed the way to more widespread and specialized charitable operations, a pattern that was followed after her death both in Europe and later in America.

Vincent de Paul was canonized in 1737, and is the patron saint of all charitable groups. Louise de Marillac was canonized in 1934, the patron saint of social works. Her example was pivotal in the pioneering efforts of the Sisters of Charity two centuries later on the frontier in Milwaukee, where her special understanding of health care needs was put into practice by members of the order patterned after the one she founded.

Early Prejudice Against Nurses

The establishment of an order of sisters in France and later in America to care for the poor was significant in many ways. Because of their vows of chastity, poverty, obedience, and service, these women lived exemplary lives and became role models of Christian service. Their education and skilled care

did a great deal to dispel the long-held belief that nurses were not professionals but little more than servants.

In the 1600s, 1700s, and even 1800s, the practice of nursing was considered an inferior occupation. Before the great nursing reforms instituted by Florence Nightingale during the Crimean War of the 1850s, hospitals were desperate places of filth and infection. As one English war correspondent wrote about the hospitals for the war wounded, "There is not the least attention paid to decency or cleanliness; the stench is appalling; the fetid air can barely struggle out."

The only exceptions to this general pattern of filth and neglect in European hospitals were those run by the Daughters of Charity, who were universally respected for their work with the sick. Equally important, in France the example set by this order began to spread a new image of women in health care. No longer was immodesty or impropriety attached to the physical care of an individual in distress.

In England, where nursing reforms were unknown until Nightingale's time, the stories of the work of the

St. Vincent de Paul and St. Louise de Marillac founded the Daughters of Charity in early seventeenth-century France. Vincent, an ordained priest, and Louise, a devout widow, met in 1625 and began to work together to help the poor. Vincent requested that Louise visit Confraternities of Charity and help establish new ones. After discovering that the proper ladies who made up the Confraternities were not suited to the physical demands of charity, Louise began to train peasant girls to perform the laborious tasks of caring for the poor. Vincent was beatified in 1729 and canonized in 1737. In 1885 he was declared the patron saint of all works of charity. Louise was canonized in 1934 and in 1960 was declared the patron saint of all social works.

Born in France, the ninth of 11 children, Catherine Labouré lost her mother when she was nine years old. One day as she stood before a statue of the Blessed Virgin, she clasped it in her arms and said, "O Mary, you must be our Mother now." After Catherine became a Daughter of Charity in 1830, the Blessed Virgin appeared to her on three occasions. When Mary appeared, Sister Catherine heard the words, "Have a medal struck on this model; all who wear it will receive great graces." Two years later the Miraculous Medal was created. Sister Catherine died in 1876 and was canonized in 1947.

Daughters of Charity in France brought great envy. (Nightingale had traveled to Paris and studied with the Daughters of Charity.) When a *London Times* reporter observed the French receiving care from women of the order, he demanded, "Why have we no Sisters of Charity?" However, Protestant England was an unlikely ground for the establishment of simi-lar Catholic sisterhoods. When the example of Louise de Marillac was followed, it was by a young Catholic woman in America, almost two centuries later. The Protestants of Europe would much later follow Louise's example with the establishment of deaconess orders among the Lutherans in Germany during the early 1800s.

St. Elizabeth Seton and the Sisters of Charity in America

Nursing in America was a virtually nonexistent art prior to the 1800s. In this rugged frontier comprised of separate colonies, women's roles in health care were performed on an individual basis by midwives in scattered communities. Upon occasion, as in Salem, Massachusetts, in 1692, those providing this minimal care were the subjects of vicious attacks, being called servants of the devil and hanged as witches. Throughout the next century and during the Revolutionary War, women who helped those in need were often derided as "camp followers" no matter what care they provided.

From the days of Louise de Marillac in seventeenth-century France to the eastern shores of the United States in the 1800s, the Daughters of Charity had remained the model order in the service of the poor. In 1809 an American widow brought the ideas of St. Vincent and St. Louise to the New World, establishing the Sisters of Charity of Emmitsburg, Maryland, patterned after the model of Louise de Marillac 200 years earlier in France.

When Elizabeth Ann Bayley was born on August 28, 1774, no one could have predicted that she would become the first native-born American saint. Born only four months after the start of the Revolutionary War, she grew up in New York City, which was occupied by British troops for several of her early years. Her family of patriots wanted change and worked to achieve it, often operating under the very noses of the British occupation.

Her wealthy Protestant family had a tradition of reform and service. Elizabeth's grandfather, a minister, had been one of the first people in the Colonies to teach in integrated classes, and to educate the children of slaves.

However, the code of behavior for women in her day required that she marry and raise a family, which she did. But other events in Elizabeth's life eventually inspired her to live among and serve the poor, and to establish the Catholic school system in the United States.

Elizabeth's father was Richard Bayley, a doctor and professor of anatomy at what is now Columbia University. He became the first inspector-general of the New York Health Department. Dr. Bayley believed in education, and Elizabeth received the best schooling available for a girl. She was also influenced by the example of her father's work doctoring among the urban poor, many of whom could not pay for his services.

Elizabeth's mother died when she was still quite young, and her father remarried. Elizabeth, as oldest daughter, helped with the care of her siblings and half-siblings. In 1794 she married William Seton, and became a mother the following year. She had four more children in the next eight years, but also began to do charity work. In 1797 she founded the Society for the Relief of Poor Widows with Small Children, which worked to alleviate the growing urban problems of women without resources. Later she expanded this idea in her adopted city of Baltimore, a port for many immigrants entering the new United States.

Elizabeth's husband was ill with tuberculosis, and they traveled to Europe with the hope of restoring his health on an ocean voyage. He died

The Miraculous Medal, created in 1832, was soon spread throughout France. By 1879, 80 million medals had been made and distributed in Paris and Lyons. The words appearing around Mary translate to: "O Mary, conceived without sin, pray for us who have recourse to thee." The reverse side shows the monogram of Mary and the hearts of Jesus and Mary, one surrounded by thorns, the other pierced with a sword.

soon after their arrival in Italy, however, and Elizabeth found herself a widowed mother with dwindling resources. She was helped by friends of her late husband, the Italian Fellicis, who introduced her to the Catholic faith. As her interest in Catholicism grew, Elizabeth's circle of Episcopalian friends became smaller in the intense climate of anti-Catholicism of the early nineteenth century. After her conversion to Catholicism in 1805, many of these people turned away from her completely. Elizabeth had only her Catholic faith and her belief in hard work to fall back on.

With the help of Catholic friends and Bishop John Carroll of Baltimore, she started a boarding school for Catholic girls, as well as a free school for poor children in the city. Like Louise de Marillac, she believed that women could benefit from education as much as men, and that training in a field of service was the highest calling. Other young women, including two of her late husband's sisters, wanted to help Elizabeth with her work. She decided to utilize the talents of the women she had helped to educate and founded the first charitable order for Catholic women in the United States in 1809.

On March 25th of that year, the feast of the Annunciation of Mary, the Sisters of Charity of St. Joseph, members of the first American religious community, made their vows. Their motherhouse was located in Emmitsburg, Maryland, near Baltimore. Nurtured by Seton until her death in 1821, the order grew steadily. Its fame in both education and nursing spread throughout the young country. It was from this central home that the sisters headed west to Wisconsin, 37 years later, to bring their creed of service to the needy and sick of Milwaukee.

After the founding of the Sisters of Charity, Elizabeth Seton continued her charitable work for many more years. In addition to teaching, she translated a dozen French books on spiritual subjects, instructed converts, corresponded with priests and bishops, and visited the poor and sick. She suffered through the deaths of her sisters-in-law and her own two daughters. But in spite of her many trials she was able to write:

> *Faith lifts the staggering soul on one side, Hope supports it on the other. Experience says it must be, and Love says— let it be.*

After Elizabeth's death, the order continued to break ground in health care by introducing compassionate care for the mentally ill in Catholic hospitals. In 1850 the American Sisters of Charity of St. Joseph and the French Daughters of Charity of St. Vincent de Paul joined together, being called varyingly the Daughters, or Sisters, of Charity thereafter, although the official new name "Daughter" and the habits of the French order were adopted. Elizabeth Seton was canonized in 1975, the first American saint.

The Wisconsin Frontier

On the Wisconsin frontier in the 1840s, there was a great shortage of women, as in most frontier settlements, and there were no nurses. The practice of medicine in early Milwaukee involved an array of unlicensed men, among whom were a few very skilled doctors surrounded by many charlatans. The situation in the early 1840s was virtually as bad as that in Paris in the 1600s. There were no medical schools, and no nursing schools. The new State of Wisconsin, in 1848, refused to consider licensing medical practitioners, and stated only that they had to belong to a county medical association.

The first medical group in the state was the Medical Society of Milwaukee County, organized in 1842 to try to control some of the wildest brands of free-lance medical practice. Four years later, when the settlement became a city, there were a great number of men who listed themselves as doctors, but few who had any real medical training at a college or under an expert practitioner.

In the East, doctors in New York were already seeking to secure passage of a pure drug law. The standard list of drugs prescribed during the 1840s and 1850s included uncontrolled substances such as Dover's powder, paregoric, hartshorn, sal rochelle, squill pills, myrrh, tartar potash, laudanum, lobelia, ergot, and febrifuge pulvules. Clearly, it was still a risky undertaking to agree to be cared for by some doctors, unless one could be certain that he was not just a pusher of pills. That assurance was hard to come by.

This free-lance atmosphere did not give rise to health care in Wisconsin much better than that in Paris in the 1600s. However, among those who were professional and skilled, the growing knowledge of contagion and the importance of quarantining the sick provided important tools that would lead them to support the creation of the city's first hospital in 1848. But these doctors couldn't do it alone. The establishment of the city's first true hospital awaited the arrival of the Sisters of Charity in Milwaukee in 1846.

The 1840s brought a growing population movement across the world, particularly the flow of people from Europe to America, and westward to

places like Wisconsin. At any period in world history, when large population movements occur, the problems with disease escalate as well. The ability of germs from one culture to find a new home in a population without immunities has led to many of the worst epidemics in history. As a great immigrant port in the 1840s, Milwaukee was susceptible to the arrival of new germs with each new shipload of immigrants that landed at the primitive wharves. Even the passage of fines for captains of lake boats or drivers of stagecoaches who brought sick people to the city did little to stem the tide of growing illnesses.

Moreover, with no hospitals to serve the needs of these immigrants, they dispersed uncontrolled and spread their germs throughout the city's entire population. By the mid-1840s a growing number of the sick went uncared-for, lived, lingered, and died on the streets, their diseases unchecked by quarantining or organized treatment. Milwaukee needed nurses and a hospital to stem this tide of sickness. The only answer was to look to the East, where a dedicated religious order was working in organized health care, notably the Sisters of Charity in Maryland.

St. Elizabeth Ann Seton was the mother of five children, including William and Richard, who served as midshipmen in the U.S. Navy. This stained-glass window shows her looking out to sea praying for her sons, who served aboard the USS Cyane. The window, located in the Blessed Sacrament Chapel of Bancroft Hall at the U.S. Naval Academy in Annapolis, Maryland, was dedicated in memory of Commander Thomas J. Donoher, CHC, USN. Father Donoher, who served in the Navy Chaplain Corps, had a strong devotion to Mother Seton. This window was dedicated to him in 1978, one year after his death.

CHAPTER TWO

From St. John's Infirmary to St. Mary's Hospital

1844–1857

Bishop Henni had only been in Milwaukee for several weeks in 1844 when he was able to see firsthand the city's many needs for social services. The pioneer town had a population of just over 10,000 people, most of them shopkeepers, traders, and day laborers, and only a few professional men. There was no hospital. There were few physicians. According to an early medical history, the first doctor to set foot in Milwaukee had to travel from Chicago to attend the ailing Mrs. Solomon Juneau, wife of the city's founding father.

A New Bishop and a City in Need

Henni's perception of the state of affairs in Milwaukee was accurate. Although many newcomers hailed the fresh lake breezes and the "healthful climate," others who looked more closely saw the growing number of bodies being hauled off to the cemetery and read in the *Sentinel* newspaper about the crowded conditions at the city's almshouse.

Henni also brought with him the knowledge of just what a charitable institution, particularly one run by the Sisters of Charity, could do in such an environment. He was acquainted with the order from his days in Cincinnati, having been ordained there in 1829, the same year that the sisters began their work in that city. He had also visited the motherhouse in Emmitsburg, Maryland, on two occasions after his arrival in America. When he accepted the call to become a priest and journey to America, Henni had arrived at the port of Baltimore where he met with the city's bishop to learn of his assignment to Cincinnati and Kentucky.

Fourteen years later, in 1843, on the eve of coming to Milwaukee, Henni attended the Fifth Provincial Council in Baltimore, where he was selected to be the bishop of the new Holy See of Milwaukee. The following spring, on March 19, 1844, Henni was consecrated bishop of Milwaukee at the cathedral in Cincinnati, by the bishops of Natchez, Pittsburgh, and Cincinnati.

Bishop Henni's selection was due, in part, to his great successes in the Ohio River city where he had worked to establish an orphanage, assist the hospital, and oversee a growing number of parishes. It was also due to the church's accurate perception that Henni's German-Swiss origins would allow him to communicate with Milwaukee's many German Catholics in their native tongue. Just two months later, on May 3, 1844, Henni arrived in the new See.

Catholic services had been held for just seven years prior to Henni's arrival in Milwaukee and he set out immediately to survey the needs of his growing congregation. There was only a small frame church, St. Peter's, located on Martin Street (today's Kilbourn Avenue) in Juneautown, just

between Jefferson and Jackson, and north of today's great Cathedral Square. Solomon Juneau, the area's first permanent resident, leading fur trader, and land speculator, had donated the land from his holdings so that the French Catholics would have a place to worship.

A Plea to the Sisters of Charity

Henni realized that the small wooden structure at St. Peter's was not sufficient to accommodate the growing number of Irish and German Catholic immigrants who had begun to flood into Milwaukee in the early 1840s. While these people fled from the potato famine or political turmoil in their homelands, they brought with them the strong desire to continue their religious traditions on Wisconsin soil. One of Henni's first actions was to begin to raise money for a new church, to be named St. Mary's, and to try to broaden the small existing program of schooling for the city's Catholic children. The cornerstone of St. Mary's on Broadway, three blocks west of St. Peter's, was laid in April 1846, and the structure was

completed the following year.

The growth of the Catholic population in Milwaukee was evidenced by the growing number of priests whom Henni attracted to minister to the city. From the original four men who met him (appointed from the Holy See in Detroit) in 1844, the number of priests serving under Bishop Henni grew to 30 by 1847. By the summer of that year Henni began to lay the foundation for the construction of a grand new cathedral for the city. St. John's Cathedral was to be built on Jackson Street, south of Martin Street.

Henni's sensitivity to the building needs of his see was only a part of his vision. He was also acutely aware, as had been Vincent de Paul and Louise de Marillac two centuries earlier, that a church building was merely one part of an entire range of needs. Providing parish schooling was another top priority and tending to the needs of the poor and the sick was another. With a distinct memory of the many good works of the Sisters of Charity from near Baltimore, Henni decided to appeal to the motherhouse in Emmitsburg, Maryland, to send to Milwaukee a group of teaching sisters so that he could open a proper parish school near the new cathedral.

On the first day of the new year, January 1, 1845, he wrote to the Venerable Mother Mary Xavier Clark, superior of the Sisters of Charity in Emmitsburg, Maryland:

Most Reverend Mother,

You will kindly permit me to approach you with a petition which has occupied my mind, since the very day of my appointment to the new See of Milwaukee—the petition to send to me, two or three of the Sisters of your Community. True, I am as yet poor—poor is everything about me; still, I believe myself tolerably prepared to receive and keep them decently, moreover, I shall indeed always be ready to divide with the Sisters the last morsel of bread I have… Be pleased then, Dear children in God, to answer as soon as you can, whether you can comply with my request… I clearly forsee, how much the labours of our good Sisters will be needed soon in this most improving part of the union. The time is not far off when we want a Hospital at this part, and before all, Asylums for poor orphans. May heaven grant to me my petitions. With the expectation of hearing soon from you, on this, to me so important a subject, I remain, with high and continued respect and veneration for you and your Community.

Yours respectfully, devoted servant in Christ, John Henni, Bishop of Milwaukee

In asking for the "labours of our good Sisters," Henni expressed his hope that if he could attract a few of the sisters to help with the small school, others

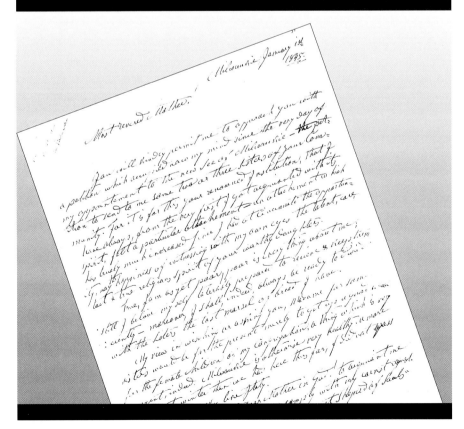

Bishop Henni's letter, dated January 1, 1845, appealed to Mother Mary Xavier Clark in Emmitsburg, Maryland, to send two or three sisters to attend to the growing needs of the Milwaukee community. Courtesy, Archives of St. Joseph's Provincial House, Emmitsburg, Maryland

The Reverend Martin Kundig, who served as Bishop Henni's vicar-general, traveled to Baltimore in the summer of 1846 to escort the sisters back to Milwaukee. Father Kundig, a missionary priest from Detroit, is noted for his efforts to further establish Milwaukee's Catholic community. Courtesy, Archives of the Archdiocese of Milwaukee

Right: *During the years 1847-1853 the Daughters of Charity lived in this building on the northwest corner of Van Buren and West Wells streets, just one block from the first location of St. John's Infirmary. The facility functioned as a school and orphanage as well as a convent.*

would follow and he could utilize these "labours" for an orphanage and also a hospital. He posted his letter, realizing that it would take from six weeks to several months to reach Baltimore, and then he waited for a reply.

The Sisters Respond

The Sisters of Charity already had experience in running hospitals and schools. Nevertheless, to ask religious women to come to a yet unincorporated city was asking a great deal, and at first the order was unable to send anyone. Bishop Henni sent another letter on June 28, 1845, repeating his hopes and his request.

However, it wasn't until early in 1846 that the motherhouse in Emmitsburg decided to send three sisters: Mary Simeon Burns, Mary Ann Paul, and Mary Agnes Frances Flanley.

Henni must have added more potency to his pleas in his second letter, written six months after the first. Perhaps he described the settlement of Milwaukee in all of its early summer beauty, or perhaps he elaborated on the need of the children for teachers and the growing problems of smallpox and tuberculosis in the area. Whatever the nature of his second appeal, it struck a chord with at least

one sister, Mary Agnes Frances Flanley, who responded with heartfelt enthusiasm: "Oh, I would like to go to such a place as that."

When he received the answer that the first three sisters were prepared to come to Milwaukee, Henni rejoiced along with his congregation. At last they would have the beginnings of a group of dedicated women to help meet the many social service needs in the area. The very next Sunday, the bishop addressed his parishioners at St. Peter's Church in what was described as a "joyful tone, a thankful outburst."

Responding to the happy news, Henni wrote back that he would send an envoy to accompany the three sisters on their westward journey. By the time these letters were transmitted back and forth from Milwaukee to Baltimore, the departure date was set for the following summer.

Bishop Henni sent his vicar-general, the Reverend Martin Kundig, to watch over the sisters on their journey to Milwaukee. They left Emmitsburg in late July 1846, and took the stagecoach to Baltimore. From Baltimore they rode the train to Buffalo, and then traveled for five weeks aboard a sailboat to Milwaukee, where they arrived on August 20. The three sisters were wel-

This painting, depicting the arrival of the Sisters of Charity in Halifax, Nova Scotia, in May 1849, reflects the style of dress worn by the sisters upon their arrival in Milwaukee the previous year. They wore black caps or bonnets with black dresses and shoulder capes as their habits until about 1850. At that time they became affiliated with the Daughters of Charity and began wearing the traditional cornettes and gray habits. Painting by Sister Agnes Berchmans, D.C.; courtesy, Mt. St. Vincent Motherhouse Archives, Halifax, Nova Scotia

Quarantine was an often-used form of treatment for illnesses. This temporary building isolated smallpox victims in 1894, much like the immigrant hospital on Jones Island was used to isolate people suffering from cholera and typhus. After St. John's Infirmary was established, it was considered to be a general hospital and not an isolation hospital. Courtesy, Milwaukee County Historical Society

Facing: *In 1845 the editor of the Milwaukie Daily Sentinel urged the establishment of a city hospital, citing that "the health of the city would be protected in a very eminent degree from all contagious diseases." Three years later St. John's Infirmary opened its doors to the sick and the poor. ©1998, Journal Sentinel, Inc. Reproduced with permission*

comed by Henni and the many priests and parishioners who had long anticipated their arrival. They alighted from the boat at Higby's Pier, near today's bridge at Clinton Street at the Milwaukee River.

Henni took the sisters by horse and wagon to 595 Jefferson Street, a small frame house he had rented and furnished for them. He made good on his promise to house them and to share with them even his last morsel of bread, and the sisters were pleased with their new surroundings, although meager and rustic. The home was two blocks northwest of the site where St. John's Cathedral would be under construction the following spring, and two blocks east of the new St. Mary's Church on Broadway where they would worship until the cathedral was completed.

Within two weeks of their arrival the sisters had started a school in the basement of St. Peter's Church, near their new home. Before the end of 1847 Bishop Henni had a small convent built facing Van Buren Street, just behind the site where the new cathedral was rising, at a cost of $625, and the sisters moved in before Christmas. A second school and a makeshift orphanage were also housed

in the new building within that year.

Much of the sisters' time was soon spent in caring for the growing number of sick among the parish, although in the early years this care took them from home to home and was a wearying drain upon their energy. By the beginning of their first spring in Milwaukee in 1847, it was apparent that the ravages of smallpox, diphtheria, typhus, and tuberculosis would soon be joined by a dreaded newcomer, cholera.

The Ravages of Disease in Early Milwaukee

The problems that Bishop Henni and the sisters witnessed first-hand stemmed from the burgeoning population in Milwaukee and the resulting mixture of germs among the people. It also originated in the government's inability to control the distribution of milk from tubercular cows, or the spread of smallpox. Local newspapers as early as the fall of 1846 had described Milwaukee as a "plague-ridden city," and had been scolded by city fathers for giving the area a bad name that might limit immigration.

In an attempt to stem the tide of these two diseases and to try to keep out the dreaded Asiatic cholera, the new city government took action that fall. In 1847 the city council directed that inoculation against smallpox (discovered only the century before) would be mandatory, and that the sale of certain foods, such as the "love apple" or tomato, would be encouraged because of their known nutritional value. However, enforcement of this regulation for inoculations among the immigrant population was very difficult because they were suspicious of Yankee doctors.

The city government also ordered that all pools of standing water would be immediately drained, and that thousands of carts of excrement from animals and open running sewers would be collected and hauled out of the city. With the removal of this waste, it was hoped, the city's wells would yield safer water for drinking and the swarming flies and maggots would spread their germs elsewhere.

They further took the step of ensuring that the poorest people (who were often those most prone to disease) would be gathered in an almshouse more than a mile north of the city limits, on a hill above the lake. It was hoped that this early, and rather cruel, form of quarantining of the poor would also remove their diseases from the center of the population. However, all of these steps taken by the city fathers, through the new board of health, were in vain as reports of disastrous cholera outbreaks as close as Chicago became more frequent. How long could they keep it out?

As the Sisters of Charity, still only three in number, walked the streets from home to home, they too understood the growing problem and feared that worse was to come. A journal entry by one of the sisters noted:

During this period care of the sick was a heavy household responsibility…Milwaukee in the early days was the chief city for the reception of immigrants. This introduced special problems in the care of the sick. Those who had not yet had time to establish homes could obviously not be cared for there.

In discussions with Bishop Henni, it was decided that the scattered treatment of the sick and dying was so inefficient that steps should be taken to establish a hospital, staffed by the sisters and visited by several of the most reputable doctors in the city. However, both Henni and the three sisters realized that they would need additional assistance from the motherhouse to carry out this plan. Once again the bishop wrote to Emmitsburg, the only source of such help that he knew of, to renew his pleas for more sisters to come to Milwaukee.

We would then most respectfully urge upon our citizens the propriety of erecting a CITY HOSPITAL. There are several very important considerations which might be urged in support of this project.— One very important one is, that the health of the city would be protected in a very eminent degree from all contagious diseases. Numbers are constantly arriving in Milwaukie from the old countries in the summer, and relentless loathsome and contagious diseases, have traced upon their sickly lineaments the most abject and indellible tracings of suffering. They land upon our shores penniless, and seek a lodging and temporary home wherever chance may direct them. They mingle with our citizens—the contagion is caught—the atmosphere is tainted—and thus often numbers are borne down with sickness which might have been prevented had the necessary precaution been used. We need

St. John's Infirmary, the Forerunner of St. Mary's

Henni began his fund-raising efforts early in the new year, 1848, and also traveled to Europe to raise money for his projects in Milwaukee, including the cathedral, an orphanage, and the hoped-for new hospital. Returning with generous donations, Henni waited for word from Emmitsburg.

His request was answered: Four more Sisters of Charity would follow the first band and come west to serve the church. Anticipating these reinforcements from their ranks, the first three sisters began making the needed arrangements to open a hospital.

It was decided that a small building near the newly rising St. John's Cathedral could serve as an infirmary. Hospitals, as we know them today, did not exist in the late 1840s. Since most doctors (and the sisters) made home visits, and since most health care was provided by relatives, the sick remained at home. The earliest so-called hospitals were actually more akin to pesthouses or almshouses, for the poorest of the poor, who could not afford to hire a caregiver, or for immigrants or other people alone in the world. They were set up more for the protection of the public health, by isolating the sick, than for the care of the individual patient.

Thus the idea of establishing a hospital in this new town was a radical one, and considered risky for the neighborhood and the caretakers. Nevertheless, Henni made arrangements to purchase a two-story frame building on the corner of Jackson and Oneida (Wells) Street, and appealed again to Emmitsburg for more sisters to work at the hospital.

Sisters Mary Agnes Felicitas Delone, Mary Agnes O'Connor, Mary Sarah Ann Butler, and Mary Bernard Gavin arrived in the early part of 1848, and with the three sisters already in the city, they began work immediately. On February 2, 1848, they made an appeal to the people of Milwaukee:

> *The Sisters of Charity of Milwaukee being provided with a suitable building will open an infirmary for the reception of invalids. They appeal to your charity for aid. The institution will be open to all citizens or strangers without distinction of class or religion or nation. It will bear the name of St. John's Infirmary of Milwaukee. Donations of furniture, household utensils, and so on will be thankfully received.*

Milwaukee's first mayor and a devout Catholic, Solomon Juneau was asked to take charge of collecting subscriptions, and the generous support of the community enabled the sisters to open the doors of this infirmary. On May 15, 1848, St. John's Infirmary, the forerunner of St. Mary's Hospital, was officially opened, just as the Territory of Wisconsin was in its final preparations for joining the Union as a new state. The Milwaukee City Medical Association appointed 12 of its members to donate time and care to the many charity cases nursed by the sisters. About 25 patients were kept before the end of that first year. But the problems quickly grew more severe.

Information about this newsworthy facility was reported in Catholic newspapers as far away as Philadelphia and Baltimore, and in the 1849 *Catholic Almanac*:

> *As the Sisters of Charity are to be the only nurses and attendants in the house, none need fear the absence of sympathy and eager vigilance… Any patient may call for any clergyman he may prefer, but no minister, whether Protestant or Catholic, will be permitted to preach to, to pray aloud before, or interfere religiously with such patients as do not ask for the exercise of his offices.*

This insistence upon freedom of religion within the walls of the new infirmary was a rather astonishing principle for the time. The Wisconsin frontier was still seen by many as a competitive religious battleground where Catholics vied with Protestants over the souls of settlers. In New York, the homeland of many of Milwaukee's Yankees, the anti-Catholic sentiment had become such a political force that a splinter political group, the "Know Nothings," had recently become active.

With the sisters, Henni reached out to sick and orphaned children with the hand of Catholic charity, in order, as he wrote, to avoid leaving "these little ones to the danger of being drawn away by Protestants." Henni's acknowledgment of the edginess between Milwaukee's Protestant and Catholic communities came as a result of a sermon just after his arrival in the city, preached against Catholics by Congregational minister J.J. Miter.

In his 1844 Thanksgiving Day sermon, Miter delivered what has been called a "rather violent and certainly uncalled-for attack on foreigners, in general, and on the Catholics, in particular, trying to show that they would not be good American citizens."

Taking Miter gently to task, Henni offered a compromise in a pamphlet titled "Facts Against Assertions," which spoke to Miter's charges. Accepting this proposal of a middle ground, Miter made peace by recanting his entire diatribe the following Sunday. Following that episode, the city's Catholic and Protestant congregations were able to work together when the need arose and the fierceness of the rivalry died down for a time.

It is even more remarkable, therefore, that the sisters insisted that religious proselytizing would not be allowed within the walls of their medical institution.

The new St. John's Infirmary was described as being "in the healthiest part of the city" and had three wards for the public, as well as some private rooms. Three more Sisters of Charity, Mary Monica Ryder, Mary Zoe Shaw, and Mary Eulalia Generosa, came to Milwaukee in 1850 to help at the hospital, school, and what would soon become St. Rose Orphanage. The motherhouse in Emmitsburg received reports from Bishop Henni, as well as letters from the sisters, about the success of their efforts in Wisconsin and about their continuing need for reinforcements to keep up the battle.

The Onset of Cholera

It was fortunate for the community that St. John's Infirmary was well established before the cholera epidemics of

When the cholera epidemic struck Milwaukee in 1849, hundreds of people lost their lives. An early prescription for treatment included using the narcotic opium and capsis or capsicum, which is found in the pepper plant. It's likely this medicinal cocktail—which eased the patient's pain and usually induced sleep—was prescribed for the most critical cases.

Top: *Asiatic cholera reached its climax in Milwaukee in 1849-1850. A record published in the* Milwaukee Sentinel *on April 27, 1850, shows St. John's Infirmary treating 28 cholera cases. ©1998, Journal Sentinel, Inc. Reproduced with permission*

Jones Island, a strip of land between the Milwaukee River and Lake Michigan, became the location for a makeshift hospital (known as the immigrant hospital) where the Daughters of Charity cared for typhus-stricken passengers of the ship Alleghany *when it arrived in 1850.*

1849 and 1850 began. Cholera is a bacteria that is spread through contaminated water, exhibits itself in gastrointestinal symptoms, and is often fatal. What was called the Asiatic cholera appeared in Europe in 1832, and began to spread to North America around 1840.

A journal kept by one of the sisters indicated that they were well aware of the dangers facing them:

> *Illness and disease was prevalent at all times and in the worst forms. Cholera epidemics swept over the state…Malaria prostrated many and took its yearly toll of life. Typhoid fever was common. Severe epidemics of smallpox were frequent and it was estimated that of those attacked, one in five died.*

By 1849 the Milwaukee Public Health Department had begun to put lime in streets and alleys to prevent the spread of disease. But pigs and horses moved up and down the alleys, and people swam their cows across the river to pasture and back every day. City workers had, by the end of March 1849, carted off a thousand truckloads of refuse, and the city council had built a bathhouse on the lake shore. But there was no sewage system to speak of, and infestation continued.

The cholera epidemic reached its peak in August 1849, and at the end of that month the board of health reported 104 fatalities out of 209 cases. Many additional cases, no doubt, went unreported. St. John's Infirmary cared for 28 people stricken with cholera, 12 of whom survived.

In 1850 the devastation of cholera continued, causing more than 300 deaths, eight of them at St. John's. An

improvised immigrant hospital was set up in buildings at the mouth of the Milwaukee River. A member of the city's board of health met incoming boats, and anyone aboard who was even suspected to be ill with cholera, typhus, or smallpox was transferred to a makeshift city infirmary right at the end of the pier. However, all attempts to stem the tide of disease and death seemed to be failing. The board of health requested the aid of the sisters in caring for the sick at this makeshift immigrant hospital, and, although already taxed to the limit, they agreed to help.

The small band of sisters, meanwhile, nursed and fed 293 patients at St. John's Infirmary between October 1, 1849, and October 1, 1850. The sisters, under the supervision of Sister Felicitas, were so poor that they could employ only one woman, Ann Campbell, for the kitchen, and had to do their own washing. Two part-time maids helped with general work. A typical Monday morning included prayers at chapel, and then work in the laundry until Mass at St. Peter's. After Mass, the patients were fed breakfast, and then the sisters returned to the washing and ironing. This daily ritual

of making cleanliness a high priority was central to the sisters' training in the procedures of health care.

The Arrival of the Plague Ship

On October 11, 1850, the propeller ship *Alleghany* arrived from Buffalo, New York, carrying about 300 Swedish and Norwegian immigrants. Many were ill with typhus, and 25 had died en route.

Some were moved to the government infirmary at the pier, and many were nursed by the Sisters (now known as the Daughters) of Charity at St. John's Infirmary. The *Alleghany*

In 1850, when typhus-stricken passengers of an immigrant ship arrived in Milwaukee, Mayor Don A.J. Upham called upon the sisters to help during the crisis. While a few of the passengers were cared for at St. John's Infirmary, most were transported to the immigrant hospital—a cluster of government buildings on Jones Island. The sisters temporarily stayed at the makeshift facility to care for the sick and dying patients. Courtesy, Milwaukee County Historical Society

became known in Milwaukee history as the "plague ship," because of the great panic that its arrival caused. Citizens, already frightened to death of newcomers bringing cholera, did not react well to the idea of a shipload of Scandinavians arriving with the dreaded lice that spread a fatal form of typhus.

Typhus, unlike cholera, is not spread by water or air but by lice. It can occur in conditions where a number of people are herded closely together, wearing the same clothes for prolonged periods, and lacking means of ensuring bodily cleanliness. It was sometimes called "gaol fever" after the British word for jail because it was believed to have originated in filthy prisons. Its symptoms included a high fever, rash, and delirium, and it killed millions of people in America well into the twentieth century. Because science had no knowledge of its cause or cure, its victims, like the victims of cholera, were offered only one treatment—quarantine.

Milwaukee Mayor Don A.J. Upham asked the Daughters to take charge of the so-called immigrant hospital during this crisis, and they obliged. At first three Daughters went each morning to this facility near the Milwaukee River, to be relieved at night by two other Daughters. After three weeks, however, it was decided that the Daughters would simply live at the temporary hospital. The Daughters faced contagion and fatigue, but were most frustrated by the language barrier that prevented them from offering spiritual comfort to their Scandinavian charges. In all, the immigrant hospital housed 260 people, only 60 of whom survived.

The diligence of the Daughters did not go unnoticed, and one historical record noted:

Through all this blackness of death two heroic physicians passed calmly along, Dr. E.B. Wolcott [later chief surgeon at St. Mary's] and Dr. C.H. Orton, with potions for the body, while the white-faced noble sisters moved silently among the sufferers with medicine for the soul.

In an outpouring of gratitude, the small band of Daughters would later be thanked by the citizens of Milwaukee, who considered their service during both the cholera and typhus emergencies to be heroic.

The Limits of Health Care

However valiant the efforts of the Daughters were, the fact remained that infirmaries or hospitals during the 1840s and 1850s were largely places where the sick could be removed from society, kept comfortable, provided with good food, clean sheets, and kind attendance by both nurses and physicians. The diseases that so threatened American cities in these decades had no known cures, and even the few available medicinal remedies were used on a "trial-and-error" basis.

While calomel was commonly administered to fever patients, one Milwaukee doctor, Dr. Enoch Chase, administered a large dose of quinine by mistake. It was reported that he then watched the patient with "considerable anxiety," hoping for the best but fearing the worst. When the quinine eased the fever and she recovered, Chase began to use quinine exclusively for all of those with high fevers.

Although the mistake turned out well for Chase and his patient, other practitioners were said to experiment with new remedies out of such desperation that one Wisconsin legislator tried to pass a law compelling "such offenders to swallow their own medicines." However, the reputable medical societies vehemently opposed the measure; one noted physician commented that he hated quackery of all sorts, both medical and political, but that the good doctors should be allowed to police their own profession.

St. John's Infirmary and the Daughters were fortunate to have doctors from the Milwaukee City Medical Association as their affiliated practitioners, and so avoided the worst of the experiments that made such headlines. This affiliation was particularly important since so many of the patients were very vulnerable, did not speak English, and had to put their full faith in trusting that the Daughters had only their welfare at heart. This trust was poignantly true for the many immigrant and poor children who were taken in at the infirmary.

Caring for Homeless Children, the Birth of St. Rose Orphanage

Although the new hospital staff struggled mightily to care for the sick, the lack of effective medicines meant that the cholera epidemic left behind many children who were suddenly orphaned by the disease. One unofficial count estimated that by the late summer of 1850, after the worst ravages were over, more than 200 children were living on their own or with relatives. Henni realized that another desperate need had to be met and he relied upon the help of the Daughters of Charity, as always, to assist him.

Henni and Milwaukee priest Father Peter McLaughlin had first presented the Daughters with the need for running a facility for the city's orphans early in 1848, even before the infirmary was completed. When one

young Irish couple, ill with fever at the immigrant hospital, realized that death was near, they summoned Father McLaughlin and begged him to care for their small daughter after their deaths. With nowhere to go with the four-year-old girl, who spoke no English and had just watched her parents die in this strange new land, Father McLaughlin took her to the Daughters' convent on Van Buren Street on May 9, 1848.

Upon answering the door, the Daughters took in their first healthy child and realized that many more such orphans would follow if the epidemics

Dr. Jeremiah Selby was the first medical student in the city, completing his preliminary medical studies in the office of Dr. John Bartlett. Selby took charge of the isolation hospital during the city's first smallpox epidemic, and during the 1850 cholera outbreak he treated many victims of the disease. He served as president of the Milwaukee County Medical Society in 1882 and remained active in medicine until his death in 1897. Courtesy, Milwaukee County Historical Society

of cholera and typhus were to continue. They decided to have a new facility built adjacent to their home and named it St. Rose Orphanage for Girls. Two years later, with more than 30 girls in residence, the Daughters and Bishop Henni solicited funding to construct a new building on Jackson Street, near the cathedral. In 1850 St. Rose Orphanage was opened, complete with dormitories, a kitchen, schoolroom, washrooms, and dining hall. This elegant new facility was used for the next 37 years, even when St. John's Infirmary was closed and the medical care facility, renamed St. Mary's

Hospital, was moved north of the city in the next decade.

Reinforcements from the East

Because of the fear of contagion, however, the Daughters who worked with the young children or taught school were not exposed to the sick patients in the infirmary and found themselves increasingly shorthanded. Appeals to the motherhouse in Emmitsburg for more assistance became more urgent after the fall of 1848, and resulted in more than a dozen additional Daughters being sent to Wisconsin in the next four years.

With the growth of the hospital and the orphanage, plus their other ongoing duties, the Daughters of Charity were in desperate need of further reinforcements. In early 1853 the motherhouse in Maryland authorized six more Daughters of Charity to travel to Wisconsin to offer support and assistance. The news that their number would soon be doubled

by these new arrivals brought great rejoicing among the Daughters, taxed to the limit by the past two years of epidemics and dying.

These six Daughters from Emmitsburg embarked on their arduous journey to Milwaukee on March 13, 1853. A number of obstacles and delays dogged them as they made their way by coach, ship, and even on foot, arriving in Milwaukee the Tuesday after Easter.

A Grateful Community

As these new reinforcements were welcomed by the Daughters in Milwaukee, the spring thaw finally came. Their numbers and energy proved to be a great help to the weary Daughters who had staffed the school, orphanage, and infirmary through the worst of the epidemics during the past four and a half years. The incidence of cholera subsided from 1851 through 1853, but typhoid and dysentery continued to take a heavy toll. Records show that the Daughters nursed several cholera cases during those years, before another deadly upsurge in 1854.

By 1854 the new Daughters were fully acclimated to both the climate and work demands of their Milwaukee environment and were able to assist with those afflicted at several institutions. They were even called to help out at the city jail, where the

An unsigned letter published in the Milwaukee Sentinel on August 22, 1856, may well have served as the impetus to begin efforts to build a new hospital in the northern part of the city. ©1998, Journal Sentinel, Inc. Reproduced with permission

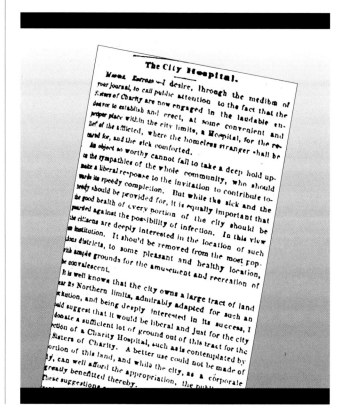

fear of cholera caused a jailbreak by inmates that fall. The city's immigrant hospital on the pier was closed in 1854, and no further cholera epidemics were reported for the next several years. Many people believed that the worst of the scourge was over at last, and praised the Daughters for all of their assistance throughout the years of its worst toll.

The winter of 1854-1855 was especially severe, however, and about 5,000 new immigrants settled in the city, so there was no lack of work for the Daughters as each new group brought cases of influenza, diphtheria, and typhoid.

St. John's Infirmary had also begun to admit people suffering from mental illness, who were not yet separated from those who had physical illnesses. Both the city and the county paid the Daughters for care of the indigent, including the mentally ill, who had nowhere else to go and were often highly susceptible to disease. In addition, a contract was signed in 1850 between the Daughters of Charity, the City of Milwaukee, and the federal Treasury Department to provide treatment for sick or disabled seamen in the port of Milwaukee. (In an effort to enlist many men for the new navy and for the much-needed merchant marine, Congress had passed a bill in 1797 that promised their health care would be provided for by federal funds, an assurance that carried over even to seamen on the Great Lakes and inland rivers of the Midwest.) This contract was renewed annually for the next 125 years.

Plans for a New Hospital

While the infirmary's patients appreciated the Daughters' efforts on their behalf, a number of neighbors were unhappy with its location, believing that it posed a threat to public health. On August 22, 1856, a letter—signed "X"—was printed in the *Sentinel* urging city leaders to donate land on the north end of town for the construction of a charity hospital to be run by the Daughters of Charity.

A committee was formed to solicit funds for the new hospital, and in a

month's time $7,000—more than half the total projected cost of the new hospital—was raised. In September a group of citizens led by attorney William H. Wright presented a petition to the city council. The petition requested a donation of land from the poorhouse farm to the Daughters of Charity. In October a subcommittee of the city council voted without dissent to select a site for the city engineer to report on and approve.

Plans were drawn by architect John Dillenberg, and the full city council approved the gift of three acres on January 10, 1857, again without dissent. Ownership of the land was transferred to the Daughters by deed on February 4, 1857. The cornerstone for the new Northpoint location of the soon-to-be-renamed St. Mary's Hospital was laid on May 15, 1857.

On January 10, 1857, the Common Council of the City of Milwaukee adopted a resolution to donate three acres of land on the northeast side of Fourth Avenue (now Lake Drive). A petition, prepared in 1856, requested that a piece of land on the north side of the city be donated as a site for the new hospital for the Daughters of Charity. This would place the "seat of pestilence" away from the more heavily populated areas. Only the Northpoint lighthouse (built in 1855), a poorhouse, and the poorfarm cemetery were located in the vicinity. The original, signed deed shown in this photo is preserved in St. Mary's archives.

CHAPTER THREE

St. Mary's on the Bluff

1857–1910

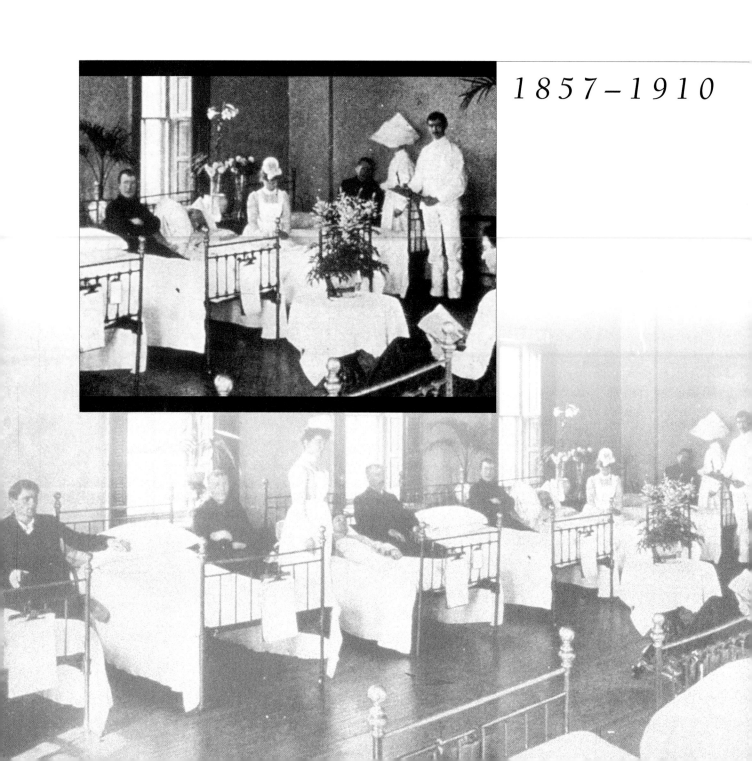

Facing: *The marine ward at St. Mary's Hospital, shown in this circa 1905 photograph, served many seamen. They showed their appreciation by performing tasks at the hospital, including carrying patients from room to room.*

AFTER A DECADE OF service to the residents of Milwaukee from the original wooden two-story building near the downtown cathedral called St. John's Infirmary, the Daughters of Charity began to dream about building a real hospital at last. The early 1850s were years of great prosperity in Milwaukee and across Wisconsin, as the state became the nation's leading wheat-growing region, and the city became the leading wheat port in the world. However, the national recession of 1857 occurred just as the hospital's plans were being finalized and the Daughters had to move forward on the promises of support from the community.

The new hospital's location was an ideal one, north of the city on an 80-foot bluff overlooking the waters of Lake Michigan. The newly christened St. Mary's Hospital at Northpoint ushered in a new era in the city's medical history.

St. John's Infirmary Becomes St. Mary's Hospital

As the patient load grew beyond the capacity of the small infirmary of St. John's, which the sisters had used since its opening in 1848, the decision was made to expand to a different location. Even without the repeated cycles of cholera epidemics, the patient load at the infirmary had continued to increase and the small building became inadequate. With more than 300 cases being treated annually, the sisters, working with Bishop Henni, made the decision to seek a new location and to erect a much larger building as a new hospital.

It was decided to name the new hospital St. Mary's, rather than St. John's, to give it a separate identity now that it would be located so far from the cathedral. In addition, the Sisters of Charity had established a tradition across the eastern United States of naming their hospitals St. Mary's. The Sisters of Charity, from Emmitsburg, Maryland, had merged in 1850 with the original order of the Daughters of Charity from France, and thereafter were called by the latter name. However, in Milwaukee, even with their new habits and crisp white-winged cornettes, many still referred to them by the name "sisters" which had already become a tradition in the city that had learned to depend on their service and kindness.

Another reason for seeking a new location was the continued opposition from neighbors to the presence of an infirmary housing those with contagious diseases in their midst. Even though the Daughters had carefully shielded their patients from contact with city residents, and had avoided spreading contagion, the problem persisted. At first, the infirmary was moved from its original location at Jackson and Wells streets, southwest to

FESTIVAL AT ALBANY HALL.—A Festival is to be given at Albany Hall this evening, in aid of the City Hospital which the Sisters of Charity are building on the North Point. The walls are all up and the roof on, but more money is needed to fit up the interior. In these hard times money can only be raised in small sums, but if all who can spare a dollar for a most worthy object will buy a ticket for the Festival to night, a handsome aggregate will be raised for the City Hospital.

Jefferson, but the proximity to the homes of many city leaders was still troubling.

Part of the opposition, no doubt, also stemmed from the fact that the Daughters, true to their vows, turned no one away, no matter how downtrodden. Most of their patients were immigrants, few spoke English, and many were seen as undesirables by the original Yankee settlers whose homes dominated the east side neighborhoods.

An Ideal Location

Working with the city's board of health, the Daughters learned that the old almshouse, located two miles north of downtown at Northpoint, was going to be moved west to Wauwatosa, making the land just beyond North Avenue at the lake bluff available for another institution. They decided that the location was perfect. It was close enough to the city to be accessible by wagon or buggy along Prospect or North avenues, or later by the new horse-drawn omnibuses, Milwaukee's first form of mass transit. In the winter people could also come by sleigh.

Moreover, the setting on the bluff was far enough from residential areas to provide a sense of safety for citizens concerned about the diseases patients might carry. In addition, the view of Lake Michigan and the fresh lake breezes made the new location seem healthy as well as scenic.

The proposed site of the hospital was a tree-covered wilderness, part of which had been a cemetery for the poor next to the old almshouse. When the three acres were given to the Daughters for a hospital, the decision was sealed. The warranty deed stated that the land would belong to the Daughters "and their heirs and assigns, forever, for a hospital; revertible, however, to the city, should the land at any time be used otherwise."

The old almshouse was leveled, and the foundation for the new brick hospital was dug early in 1857. Contracts for the construction of the hospital were signed by April 22, 1857, and the work began. The building's foundation measured 82 feet in length and 53 feet wide in the center, with three stories to be erected at a height of 47 feet in the wings and 53 feet in the center section.

The construction workers were assisted by Sister Monica Ryder, a tall and strong woman who had nursed typhus victims at the immigrant hospital. She helped the men dig out stumps, and spent six weeks painting the interior of the building once it was erected. She also continued her rounds of nursing, tending the sick while building for the future.

With the natural beauty of the location, it seemed important to surround the new building with as many plants and trees as possible and Sister Ryder created a design for the grounds, including many new trees and shrubs as well as a vegetable garden. The new property had once been an enclosed cow pasture for the almshouse, and so the ground was very fertile and her many flowers and plants soon flourished.

The Recession of 1857

Soon after the foundation for the new hospital was begun, the nation experienced a severe recession in 1857. Cotton prices fell, bonds on the New York stock market plummeted, and many Wisconsin bondholders felt the extreme financial pinch. Many banks failed and it was a difficult time to raise money for a new hospital venture.

The intentions of those who donated to the new hospital were good, but a number of those who pledged financial support were unable to actually give it. As a result, the Daughters organized a fall festival, which was held on October 29, 1857. This was the first and last time that the Daughters employed this method of fund raising. Net proceeds amounted to more than $1,000, which was a large sum for a festival but far less than they needed, especially with all of the hard work it took to produce it. As a result, when the Daughters moved into the new hospital in 1858, they brought with them an $11,000 debt.

A New Source of Revenue

However, by March 11 of the following year, when the Daughters of Charity of St. Joseph's in the City of Milwaukee were officially chartered by the Secretary of State of Wisconsin, the debt had already been greatly reduced. The hospital was able to pay off the debt and balance its books before 1860 through the support of paying patients, the donations of several denominations of churches from around the city, and the $15,350 in appropriations from the State of Wisconsin for its attendance to the paupers of the city.

The Daughters took the step of being incorporated under the laws of the State of Wisconsin to protect themselves as a distinct entity as they operated the hospital. Throughout the country, wherever they had established similar hospitals, the Daughters of Charity from Emmitsburg had also incorporated to provide themselves both the corporate ability and the legal protection afforded by state law. In their incorporation papers, they listed as the purpose of their corporation the need to "afford a greater opportunity…for the establishment of hospitals, schools, asylums, and other institutions for the relief and education and care of the poor, the needy, the destitute, the orphan, and the ignorant."

Sisters Mary Vincent McEntee, Mary Frances Agnes Flanley, Mary George Sebold, Arianna Buckley, and Monica Ryder were members of the original corporation. They duly elected officers and created by-laws on September 5, 1859, and met to make major decisions about the hospital and to send reports of these decisions, as well as a balance sheet, to the Daughters of Charity motherhouse in Maryland.

Working together as a board, the Daughters kept track of all expenses, including those in running the small pharmacy where the Daughter in charge mixed medicines as prescribed by common practice or as dictated by the attending physician. By the late 1850s the Daughters of Charity from Emmitsburg and their splinter groups had established most of the non-military hospitals in the United States, including ones in Baltimore, Philadelphia, Cincinnati, Milwaukee, Louisville, St. Louis, and New Orleans.

The New St. Mary's Hospital

The attractive new hospital was made of unpressed brick, with a large basement, and three stories above the ground. It had six wards, 10 private rooms, an office, a chapel, and rooms for the Daughters and for the hired help. Its normal capacity was 55

Facing: *Nearly six months after the cornerstone was laid for St. Mary's Hospital at its new Northpoint location, the Daughters held a fund-raiser after some promises of financial support were not fulfilled. ©1998, Journal Sentinel, Inc. Reproduced with permission*

Below: *Although the sisters worked long hours running the hospital—usually from 4 a.m. until 9 p.m.—occasionally there was time for a walk down to the pier that stood in the waters of Lake Michigan. Sister Gertrude, interviewed for a 1932 Milwaukee Sentinel article, talked of waving to passengers on the pleasure boats that traveled up to Whitefish Bay. She remembered, "It was so quiet over the lake, you could hear them laughing and talking." This circa 1890 illustration depicts a similar scene along the shores of the lake.*

Postcards, which became quite popular at the turn of the century, often depicted standard scenes of a particular city or area. The water tower provides a scenic backdrop for St. Mary's Hospital in this postcard, which shows the 1858 structure. The picturesque card would have cost the sender a penny to mail anywhere in the United States, Cuba, Canada, or Mexico.

patients, and each floor was equipped with the latest in baths and water closets. The three largest wards measured 30 by 30 feet; the smaller three were 18 by 14 feet. In addition to the main building, there were outhouses and a barn on the property for horses and a few cows.

The official transfer of the Daughters and their patients to the new St. Mary's Hospital took place on November 24, 1858. Bishop Henni,

whose foresight had brought about this institution and its workers, was on hand to bless the chapel. The chapel on the second floor at the building's center was a simple one for use by any patient who wished to pray or attend services.

However, it was central to the strong principles of the Daughters of Charity, and greatly to their credit, that no one under their care would be compelled to receive a priest or minister or

St. Mary's Hospital, circa 1908.

to attend services. As before, the Daughters were proud of the fact that they offered their care to persons regardless of religion, ability to pay, or color. It was a rare inclusiveness during a time when racism and religious disputes still played a major part in American life.

At first all of the building's water came from a deep well. In later years the city's first water tower at Northpoint (erected in 1873) would assure the hospital of a ready supply of pure drinking water, an important feature in the years of continuing epidemics. Below the bluff, at the Lake Michigan shore, was the long stretch of beach later christened McKinley Beach, along which, even in the 1850s, the area's residents could stroll for a healthy outing.

With the nursing staff housed comfortably at this new location, the nurses could enjoy the spaciousness

This lithograph depicts the still somewhat secluded landscape near St. Mary's Hospital seen behind the Milwaukee Water Works (now Northpoint Pumping Station) in 1873. This northwest view today would look from Lincoln Memorial Drive and the eastern portion of North Avenue. Attributed to Louis Kurz; courtesy, Collection of Thomas Beckman

of the specialized wards, which were divided according to medical problems. The larger wards were used for the many patients who were charity cases, as well as for sailors who were subsidized by federal funds, while the smaller private rooms were set aside for special cases and for paying patients. The hospital's loyal and hard-working doctors were just as pleased with the new facility as were the Daughters of Charity and looked forward to serving patients in the most modern medical facility in the city.

The Medical Staff

The doctors who had served at St. John's Infirmary were also busy at the Northpoint site. Dr. Azariah Blanchard, Dr. Jeremiah Selby, and Dr. John Dousman continued their work with the marine ward, as well as treatment of the mentally ill. Dr. John K. Bartlett, a graduate of Yale University and New Haven Medical School, was also on the staff of St. Mary's. A well-educated progressive, Bartlett strongly believed in public education and worked to advance public sanitary conditions.

Blanchard, a graduate of Geneva Medical College in New York, had come to Milwaukee in the mid-1840s, following his daughter, Mary Blanchard Lynde, who traveled west from New York with her new husband, attorney William Pitt Lynde. Lynde was later mayor of Milwaukee and congressman from Wisconsin, while his father-in-law, Azariah Blanchard, became one of the city's most respected doctors during his two decades in medical practice before his death in 1868.

Another one of the hospital's early

physicians, Dr. Charles H. Orton, had come to Milwaukee after medical studies at Queens College, Canada, not far from his home in Erie, Pennsylvania. Orton, who served many years at St. Mary's, was chosen to lead both the city and the county medical societies for several terms during the 1850s and 1860s. He was also selected by the federal government to head the "Marine Hospital," the name given to the special ward at St. Mary's for sailors and seamen.

Because most of the attending physicians at St. Mary's, as at the old infirmary, were sent by an official agreement with the Milwaukee City Medical Association, they were often better trained than the average practitioner and more able to avoid some of the worst of the questionable medical procedures of the day. In fact, one of the leaders of the staff at St. Mary's, Dr. Erastus B. Wolcott, a graduate of the Medical College of Western New York, earned acclaim for a new surgical procedure in 1861.

An Important Event

Wolcott, a railroad developer and owner of the city's first flour mill, was also an outstanding surgeon, whose deftness of procedure was respected by the Daughters who attended his patients and by his colleagues in medicine. A great act of medical pioneering took place at St. Mary's on June 4, 1861, when Dr. Wolcott performed the first successful removal of a kidney ever recorded. Wolcott was assisted by Dr. Charles Stoddard, and the patient lived for 15 days after the surgery. At that time, operations were far from antiseptic procedures. That the 58-year-old patient, whose kidney was tumorous, survived for as long as he did without antibiotics is nothing short of miraculous.

This photo of the water tower was probably taken shortly after its completion in 1874. The tower and the original St. Mary's Hospital were considered to be remotely situated until other buildings including St. Rose Orphanage were constructed in later years. Courtesy, Milwaukee County Historical Society

The hospital register served as a record of patients admitted from 1859 through the early 1900s. Rheumatism, typhoid fever, malaria, and measles were just a few of the illnesses afflicting the city's population.

Right: *When St. Mary's opened at its site adjacent to the water tower, the first register listed patients by name and country, preserving the history of the hospital's early years as well as serving as a record of Milwaukee's early ancestry. The book remains on display at St. Mary's today.*

Wolcott was honored for his achievements and for his many contributions to the field of medicine by being selected a surgeon general of the Wisconsin State Militia, a regent of the new University of Wisconsin, and a representative from the state to the 1867 International Exposition in Paris. He served as a lead surgeon during the Civil War and was elected to head the Wisconsin State Medical Society several times.

Hospitals and the Civil War

During the first two years of the Civil War, from 1861 to 1863, St. Mary's was the only hospital in the state of Wisconsin caring for sick or wounded soldiers. The average number of soldiers in-house averaged between 50 and 80 per day, with 110 the highest recorded on one day. The corridors of the hospital were jammed with cots, due to St. Mary's proximity to the military receiving center for Milwaukee, Camp Sigel, which was located at Royall near Lafayette Place. After three other hospitals in Wisconsin opened to serve soldiers by 1863, the number of wounded soldiers at St. Mary's diminished, to between 20 and 30 a day.

The year 1863, however, was the bloodiest of the war, with Wisconsin's troops occupied under General Grant at Vicksburg, as well as with the Union Army at the great battle of Gettysburg. After a visit to President Lincoln by Cordelia Harvey, the wife of Wisconsin's governor, the federal government accelerated its program of sending wounded soldiers home to be cared for in local institutions, finding the mortality rate at army field hospitals alarmingly high. And so, trains carrying Milwaukee's sons returned

from many bloody battlefields during the final two years of the war before its end in 1865. As these trains rolled into the station they were met by horse-drawn ambulances that conveyed them to St. Mary's or to the new Passavant Milwaukee Hospital on the city's west side.

Throughout the war, St. Mary's continued its covenant to care for the poor and admitted all cases, "mental as well as physical," making no restrictions on account of "race, color, creed, or nation." An examination of the hospital register of 1859-1865 bears this promise out, although the majority of patients listed were still Irish. Insanity and consumption (tuberculosis) were

the diseases most frequently listed, but the survival rate was good. Out of 36 patients admitted during one six-month period, only three died, a hallmark in these days before the advent of modern medicine and a tribute to the curative ability of constant care.

A Mission to Serve the Poor

Throughout the 1850s and thereafter, the State of Wisconsin, as well as Milwaukee County, paid the Daughters of Charity for care of the indigent. More than $15,000 was paid by the state treasury to St. Mary's Hospital between 1862 and 1872. Despite the fact that most of the nursing was done by the Daughters, who received no wages for their labor, costs still exceeded revenues, and the hospital posted a small deficit every year. The Daughters labeled their indigent patients the "representatives of God." According to staff physician Charles H. Orton, many charity cases were sent to St. Mary's Hospital and not one was ever refused.

On November 26, 1860, city aldermen passed a resolution donating an additional seven-tenths of an acre of land to the Daughters for hospital

Dr. John B. Dousman began practicing in Milwaukee in 1842 and offered his services to the sisters at St. John's Infirmary and later St. Mary's Hospital. Dousman, who earned his medical degree in Boston and New York, also served as president of the Wisconsin State Medical Society. He continued his work in Milwaukee until his death in 1868.

Dr. John K. Bartlett, one of Milwaukee's prominent physicians, provided his services to St. John's Infirmary in 1849. He continued his practice with the hospital when the sisters moved to the new site overlooking Lake Michigan. A graduate of Yale College, Bartlett was considered progressive in his practice of medicine. He also was an advocate of obtaining a thorough medical education, forming a public library, and improving sanitary conditions. Bartlett practiced in Milwaukee from 1841 to 1889.

Sisters treated Civil War soldiers on the battlefield and off, putting themselves at risk for injury or even death, as depicted in this painting by an unknown artist titled "The Innocent Victim." Although it portrays a "Sister of Charity killed by a stray bullet," no sisters were killed on the battlefield during the Civil War. They did, however, witness the ravages of war as they struggled to treat the burgeoning numbers of sick and wounded soldiers who filled St. Mary's during and after the war. Courtesy, St. Joseph's Provincial House Archives, Emmitsburg, Maryland

The Daughters of Charity were ever present during conflicts of the nation as seen in this photo taken at Camp Wikoff in Long Island, New York, during the Spanish-American War. This war directly touched Milwaukee—including when soldiers from Wisconsin's 1st and 2nd Regiments were cared for at St. Mary's. Courtesy, St. Joseph's Provincial House Archives, Emmitsburg, Maryland

purposes. This land was adjacent to the grounds of the hospital and added to the spaciousness of the hospital campus, the welcoming sweep of the long entry circle, and the potential for future additions on the large bluff overlooking the lake.

When the city council considered a proposal to take back some of its land, donated years earlier to the hospital, an emotional debate resulted. Many residents remembered the fact that only the Daughters of Charity had stepped forward on many occasions to assist the city in the crisis of epidemics and did not want to see land stripped away

from them, merely for convenience. Following on the heels of the hospital's move out of the city to the north shore and the reach of the city omnibus lines up Prospect and Farwell avenues, many residents decided to build large new homes along the bluff near the hospital. To serve these new developments in 1890, the city council decided to construct a new street along the top of the bluff, called Terrace Avenue.

At issue was a strip of land given to the Daughters in 1860, which the city needed for the new street. Terrace Avenue, as planned, would have to be built over the hospital property, making the land owned by the Daughters less suitable for any other use. Minutes of the hospital board show that the Daughters were originally offered $13,000 for the land in 1891, but various city officials opposed this price as too high.

In February 1900 the city agreed to construct the street so as to take the least amount of hospital land and also to pay the Daughters of Charity $5,000 for their small loss of property. It was a fair settlement and was completed in the midst of another wartime medical crisis, the Spanish-

American War, which once again highlighted how much the city, the state, and the country depended upon its valued hospitals.

Steam Heat

Even though the hospital grounds had many wooded sections and Downers' Woods was only a mile to the north, the cost of heating the entire facility through wood-burning stoves each winter soon became a burden. In the last decades of the nineteenth century, new techniques in central heating came to American homes and public facilities. Centralizing the combustion process in a large basement furnace was not only more economical, it was also much safer than hauling wood to separate stoves in each ward and disposing of the ashes.

In 1868 steam heat was introduced into the hospital through the work of one of its grateful former patients, James C. Henderson Judge, a native of Ireland. Judge had lost his sight in an accident while blasting in a stone quarry and for several months

had received the Daughters' care for his painful facial wounds. After his discharge from the hospital, the Daughters decided to employ him, putting his interest in mechanical experiments to use. His first improvement was a boiler, installed in the kitchen to ensure a steady supply of hot water.

He designed his next innovation by carefully feeling his way through the hospital with his cane to obtain accu-

This surgical kit was used by one of Milwaukee's renowned surgeons in the mid- to late 1800s—Dr. Nicholas Senn. While Dr. E.B. Wolcott was performing surgeries at St. Mary's Hospital, Senn was doing the same at Milwaukee Hospital. Courtesy, Medical Society of Milwaukee County

Dr. E.B. Wolcott (far left), a practicing physician and surgeon in Milwaukee from 1839 to 1880, was one of the first members of the Milwaukee County Medical Society and helped found the Milwaukee City Medical Association in 1845. He married the first woman to practice medicine in Milwaukee, Dr. Laura J. Ross (left), in 1869. She overcame many obstacles to become a consulting physician at St. Mary's Hospital and other local institutions while also establishing a large and successful practice. Courtesy, Milwaukee County Historical Society

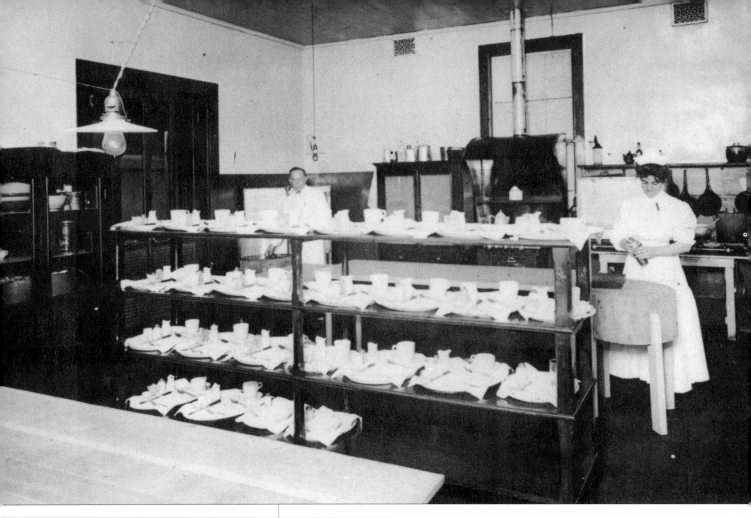

Hospital food service was provided by regular staff at St. Mary's and a few hired domestics. St. Mary's nurses (as seen in this early 1900s photo) and the Daughters often worked in the kitchen preparing meals for the patients.

rate dimensions. He then carved wooden models for the boiler, safety devices, heaters, and a network of pipes. The system used 35 tons of coal a year, and cost about $3,500. It was so efficient that a state legislative committee on an inspection tour of the hospital recommended its use for state institutions.

The January 24, 1868, edition of the *Milwaukee Daily News* praised the steam boiler, as well as the "scrupulous cleanliness of every part of the premises." Fastidiousness had been a crucial part of the principles adopted by the Daughters since their first years in hospital work, and remained crucial as they branched out into new areas of medical care in the late nineteenth century.

One of the aspects of receiving state funding was the annual hospital visit by a state team of inspectors. Among the many things for which St. Mary's was commended was its great attention

to cleanliness, described in one visitor's report as excellent and highly admirable. The hospital's floors were so white, the team reported, that "not one single particle of dirt could be discovered in any crack or corner, or a single stain upon wall or woodwork."

Moreover, the team assured the legislature that this high standard of sanitation was not just occasional, but the "usual order of things." When the time came to consider opening a maternity program, this extensive cleanliness was crucial.

Ministering to Mothers

The number of patients continued to grow, and the Daughters expanded their range of services. The first baby was born at St. Mary's in 1875, a highly unusual event for a time when doctors attended births in private homes. Many people still believed that a hospital was a place where the poor, and a few others, went to die, but few thought of it as a place to be born.

However, doctors could not always attend to the many women of the city who could ill afford their fees, even though a typical birth attendance cost only about five dollars in the 1870s. Compared to 10 cents for a loaf of bread or 23 cents for a dozen eggs, the amount was unthinkable for many. For women without relatives, or even the means to pay a midwife, the idea of hospital care for themselves and a newborn began to be more appealing. A *Milwaukee Daily News* editorial in 1875 pointed out the need for a "lying-in hospital for distressed and helpless women upon whom the responsibilities of maternity have come without such home provision as humanity requires at that season of suffering."

Sister Mary Vincent, "that indefatigable minister of mercy," started a cam-

paign to raise money to convert one ward to a lying-in facility. She collected money during the remainder of 1875, before being called back to assist at the motherhouse in Emmitsburg. As the campaign continued, the *Milwaukee Daily News* mentioned that "the bulk of

By the late 1800s Milwaukee had become a bustling city, as shown in this 1880s photograph. At about the same time, St. Mary's was experiencing its own growth—an increase in patient population—prompting the construction of a 68-foot addition. Courtesy, Milwaukee County Historical Society

the amount collected up to this moment has been contributed by Protestant ladies and gentlemen." It urged all of Milwaukee's citizens, Catholics in particular, to heed the call for assistance to create a place where abandoned women, or unwed mothers, could give birth in safety.

As a result of the Daughters' foresight, St. Vincent's Infant Asylum, which also housed unwed mothers, was opened in 1877. Orphaned and abandoned babies up to the age of six then went to St. Joseph's Orphanage, run by the parish of St. John's, where it was hoped they would be adopted. Girls over the age of six were cared for by the Daughters of Charity at St. Rose's Orphanage, which had been established next to the infirmary in 1848. Boys were cared for at St. Aemilian's Orphanage, which was run by an order of religious men.

A New Wing
The patient census doubled during the 1880s, and plans were made for a new wing on the south end of the hospital. With many prominent physicians and businessmen among its sup-

Left: *Alexander Mitchell (1817-1887), a leader in business and development in the Milwaukee community and a philanthropist, pledged money over the years not only to help build the original St. Mary's Hospital, but to fund the south addition in 1888. A $5,000 bequest left to St. Mary's upon his death in 1887 allowed construction of the new addition to begin. Courtesy, Milwaukee County Historical Society*

City Water Tower 1873 | South Addition 1888 | Main Wing 1858

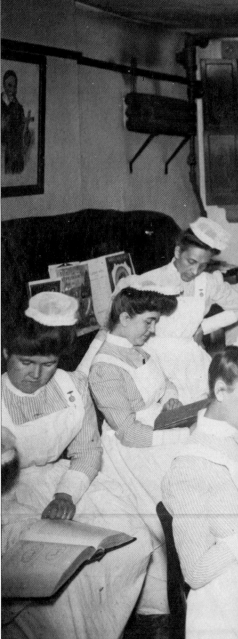

In 1888 a south wing was constructed, expanding the 55-bed hospital to 80 beds. The addition was needed after the number of patients nearly doubled in the latter part of the 1880s.

The Reverend Patrick J. Donahoe became St. Mary's first resident chaplain after retiring from his position as pastor of St. Peter's Church in 1880. Known to many as "Father Donahoe," he served at St. Peter's during the cholera outbreak in 1854 and later assisted in funeral ceremonies held at St. John's Cathedral for victims who died when the steamer Lady Elgin *sank off the shores of Lake Michigan in 1860. Just five years before his death, Father Donahoe earned the title monsignor, an honor bestowed upon him by Pope Leo XIII.*

porters, St. Mary's was able to reach out into the greater Milwaukee community to solicit donations for its much-needed expansion. Leading banker and railroad executive Alexander Mitchell had long supported several charitable institutions in the city, including St. Mary's. A Scotsman and a Presbyterian, Mitchell recognized the many deeds done by the Daughters of Charity that benefited the entire city. He had lived through the terrible epidemics and, like many grateful citizens, he never forgot the Daughters' valiant nursing efforts.

When Mitchell died in the spring of 1887, he left a $5,000 bequest to St. Mary's Hospital in gratitude for these years of service. His bequest, plus the generous donations of other Milwaukeeans who followed suit, made the hope for a new hospital wing become a reality. The new wing was blessed on March 8, 1889, by Archbishop Michael Heiss. It provided more private rooms, wards, an operating room, stairways, and an elevator.

Built as a virtual replica of the original 1858 architecture, the new wing was attached on the south end of the old building, so that they appeared to be one structure. The massive appearance of the new facility, still in a modified French style, was a testimony to the fact that St. Mary's

Hospital had become one of the city's most valued and premier medical institutions, far removed from the indifferent wooden structure of four decades before.

Doctors for the Soul

Priests at St. Peter's or St. John's Cathedral conducted Mass for the Daughters, as did Father Kundig and Bishop Henni from time to time. St. Mary's first resident chaplain was the Reverend Patrick J. Donahoe, who had been pastor at St. Peter's from 1853 to 1880. Upon his retirement, he came to St. Mary's and served as chap-

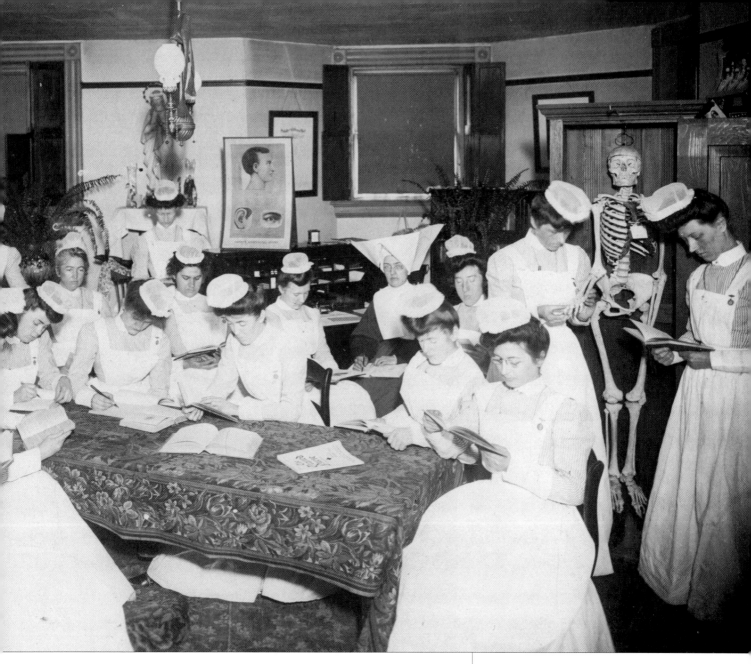

lain for the next nine years. Father Donahoe, himself an Irish immigrant, had ministered to many during the infamous cholera epidemic. He was active in the Temperance Movement, and was a theologian well respected by other priests and bishops.

With the official presence of priests for any patients who wanted to call upon them, St. Mary's offered patients and families whatever spiritual comforts they needed. However, the ongoing spiritual quality of mercy exhibited by the nursing Daughters may well have been the most comforting presence of all.

St. Mary's Training School for Nurses

Before the turn of the century, American society began an accelerated emphasis on technical excellence and on training. For the nursing profession, this meant not just an apprenticeship program, as the Daughters of Charity had always offered, but a more formalized nursing school akin to the many colleges for women opening their doors across the country.

In New York, the first nursing school in the country—at Bellevue Hospital—began classes in 1873 and by 1880 there were 15 more. The real

Nursing students had classroom work, but also heard lectures and practiced nursing at the hospital. By 1905 students had access to a suitable medical library. The students in this circa 1907 photo gather to study their coursework.

St. Mary's Training School for Nurses—later St. Mary's School of Nursing—opened in 1894 and graduated its first class in 1896.

By the turn of the century nursing students no longer wore the white uniforms trimmed in blue, but dressed in striped uniforms with bibs.

blossoming of opportunity for skilled nursing education, however, came in the 1890s, when more than 430 additional nursing schools were established around the country.

Sister Loretto Vaughn, hospital director at St. Mary's in the 1890s, was responsible for starting St. Mary's Training School for Nurses in 1894. Requirements were "a healthy body, an alert mind, and a capacity for punctuality and strict obedience to orders." The requirements stipulated that an applicant should have a "fair English education, and should be able to write legibly, to take note of lectures, and to keep accurate, simple accounts."

After one or two months' probation, nurses received eight dollars per month for personal expenses, as well as room and board. Their education was provided in exchange for their services. The course of training included instruction in practical nursing, weekly lectures by physicians and surgeons, food and bandage preparation, and examinations. Student nurses rose at 5:30 in the morning, and lights out was at nine at night. The first graduating class, in 1896, included seven lay nurses and nine sisters. A total of 131 nurses graduated from the school between 1896 and 1914. The nursing school would remain open for the next 75 years, providing both the hospital and Wisconsin many hundreds of highly skilled nurses in a variety of specialized fields.

Medical Breakthroughs at the Turn of the Century

While the nurses' training taught the young women the rudiments of known hygiene and the discipline of skilled care, it also imparted to them the fundamentals being discovered in the rapidly changing world of medical science. Between 1858, when the first St. Mary's Hospital was erected, and the blossoming of the nursing program 40 years later, many discoveries had advanced knowledge in the field of medicine.

The theory that a doctor's obstetric instruments could actually spread a deadly childbed contagion, called "puerperal fever," had been published by Boston physician Oliver Wendell Holmes, Sr. There were many advances in anesthesiology, which took the field from the earliest era of laughing gas to the invention of a mask inhaler using a blend of oxygen and nitrous acid in the 1860s.

Advances in medical knowledge and surgical techniques became more wide-

A 1947 reenactment of turn-of-the-century care at St. Mary's depicts a nurse wearing the traditional stripe and apron uniform and a sister wearing the traditional cornette and gray dress.

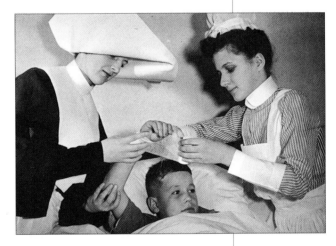

Left: *Since its inception, St. Mary's Training School for Nurses operated under the guidance and protection of the Blessed Virgin Mary. To honor her, school director Sister Loretto Vaughn suggested that the first students of the school wear creamy white uniforms with blue trim.*

spread after 1880, when the curator of the Army Medical Museum and Library, John Shaw Billings, began to publish the *Index Medicus*, which provided for doctors and nurses everywhere a listing of articles about the newest discoveries in medical science. The index was called a "monumental bibliography of medical literature."

Cleanliness in the operating room was enhanced by the use of rubber gloves, first introduced by William Halstead in 1890. The fight against tuberculosis was advanced by work at the Saranac Sanitarium in New York State, and in 1895 the X-ray was first used as a diagnostic tool. As better microscopes became available and as funding for medical research grew, there were many breakthroughs at the turn of the century, including the isolation of a bacillus that caused gangrene and the discovery of the cause of yellow fever. Howard Taylor Ricketts demonstrated that typhus fever was caused by a class of organisms carried by a tick or a louse. Moreover, both X-ray and radium treatments for breast cancer were first begun in 1896.

Sisters were present throughout a patient's care, as seen in this 1905 photograph of a hospital dressing room.

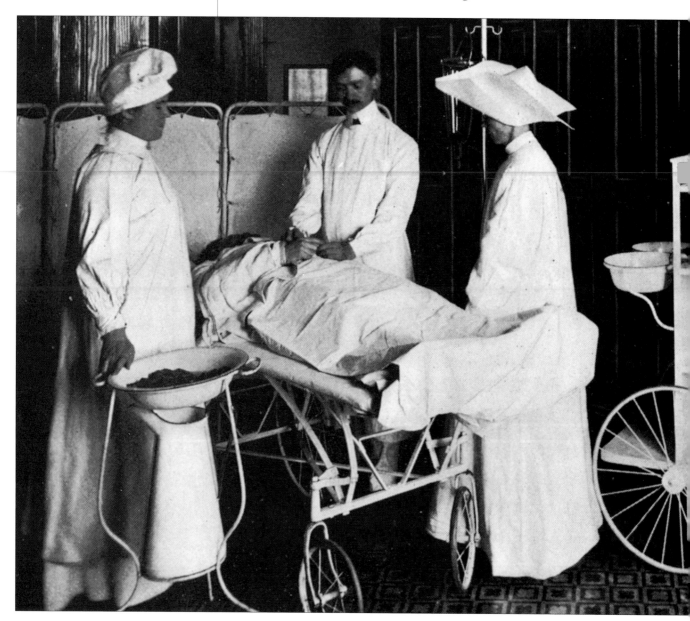

An Official Medical Staff

The nurses and physicians on the hospital staff continued their daily efforts to treat patients in the best way they knew how. The first formal staff of physicians at St. Mary's was organized in 1899. Dr. Solon Marks was chief surgeon and medical supervisor. There were four other attending doctors and 11 members of the "visiting staff."

Dr. Rupert Blue, who was later to become surgeon general of the United States Health Service, took charge of the marine hospital ward in 1900. Dr. Blue kept many cases at St. Mary's

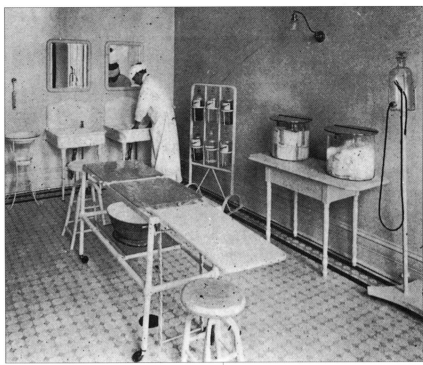

in Milwaukee when previously most had been sent to Chicago. The sailors and soldiers showed their appreciation by helping as porters, waiters, and laundrymen. Their assistance was especially useful before the construction of the 1909 building, as the old hospital had no elevator and patients had to be carried from room to room or between floors.

While operations were being performed well before the turn of the century, aseptic surgery in Milwaukee was still in its infancy when this photograph of an operating room was taken for the 1905 annual report.

Left: *A practicing physician in Milwaukee from 1873 to 1891, Dr. Nicholas Senn was one of the city's prominent physicians, renowned for his work in surgery and plastic surgery. His work early in his career was described as "daring" but was later heralded by his colleagues. He wrote many books including* Experimental Surgery; Principles of Surgery; *and* Pathology and Surgical Treatment of Tumors. *In 1888 he was appointed surgeon general of Wisconsin and held that position until he left the state in 1893. Courtesy, Milwaukee County Historical Society*

After three years of military service during the Civil War, Dr. Solon Marks came to Milwaukee and established himself as a renowned surgeon. Some of his work received national attention, including his removal of a bullet that was embedded in a patient's heart region for six years. He practiced in Milwaukee from 1864 to 1914, serving as chief surgeon at St. Mary's Hospital in 1866. Courtesy, Milwaukee County Historical Society

Far right: In 1898 St. Mary's held a commemorative service celebrating the hospital's 50th anniversary. The hospital had evolved from being St. John's Infirmary, located on the corner of Jackson and Oneida streets downtown, to become St. Mary's Hospital and St. Mary's Training School for Nurses, now overlooking Lake Michigan at its Northpoint location. ©1998, Journal Sentinel, Inc. Reproduced with permission

Facing: Sister Dolores Gillespie was a native of Chicago. Before coming to Milwaukee she taught school in New Orleans and served as a nurse in the Spanish-American War. She became superintendent of St. Mary's in 1904 and was responsible for construction of the east facility.

The Coming of a New Century

Sister Dolores Gillespie became superintendent of St. Mary's in 1904, and focused her dreams on the idea of building an entirely new hospital on the hill. The old facility, even with its 1888 addition, had seen hard service for almost 50 years. Raising money was difficult, however, and many area banks refused to lend the hospital money because of the Panic of 1907. Banks cited the fact that St. Mary's was a poor risk because it carried so many charity cases.

However, Sister Dolores was an able financial manager, and through careful borrowing, investing, and stewardship of corporate donations and legacies she was able in 1907 to hire an architect and expert in hospital planning from Chicago. The old building had been declared beyond remedy by city inspectors and not worth the expense of repairing.

Pushing forward with great faith, she led the team at St. Mary's into the twentieth century and the construction of a brand-new building on the hill to serve the hospital's continuing mission.

FIFTY YEARS IN EXISTENCE

ST. MARY'S HOSPITAL COMPLETES HALF A CENTURY OF USE-FULNESS.

HISTORY OF A BENEVOLENT IN-STITUTION THAT HAS DONE MUCH GOOD.

A COMMEMORATIVE SERVICE MON-DAY TO WHICH ALL FRIENDS ARE INVITED.

Fifty years ago the great hospital that recently won the gratitude of Milwaukeeans by turning its hallways and reception rooms into wards for the expected sick soldiers was established and for the half century past has been the haven of rest for the weary and sore of body, the afflicted and the injured.

In 1848, when Milwaukee was a little, struggling municipality, which had arrived at the dignity of cityhood but three years before, and when the great state of Wisconsin was only five months old, the Sisters Felicita, Agnes, Bernard and Mary Paul, who had come to Milwaukee at the invitation of Bishop Henni, opened St. John's infirmary. Nov. 12 was the day of the opening and the first hospital in Milwaukee was established. The original building was on the southeast corner of Jackson and Oneida streets, where the residence of the late Dr. William Fox now stands.

Most of the surgeons of the city were on the staff of the new hospital and its support came from all parties and creeds. The patients cared for were of all kinds, no distinction of creed being made. The work of the hospital grew at such a rate that in 1852 it was removed to more commodious quarters on Jefferson street.

In 1856 the present hospital was built on land that had been donated by the city for the purpose. The feeling in regard to the giving of the land for the hospital was universally favorable, as the people of the city realized the need of a hospital and recognized the good work that St. John's infirmary was doing. This feeling was largely engendered by the action of Sister Felicita and her assistants, who visited the passengers and crew of a schooner which came into port with the cholera on board and was shunned by all others. The sisters took the afflicted to a house near the beach, and cared for them until their recovery. Only sixty of the 300 afflicted persons who were taken with the plague before its course was stopped recovered. In 1855 a committee among whom were G. M. Fitzgerald, Edward O'Neil, A. H. Johnston and Garnett Barry undertook the work of raising funds for the new building. Among the subscribers to the fund were Bishop Henni, D. G. Power, W. E. Cramer, J. B. Martin, Alexander Mitchell, Joshua Hathaway, J. B. Cross, Hans Crocker, Byron Kilbourn, J. H. Rogers, Rufus King, J. H. Tweedy, W. P. Lynde, Marshall & Ilsley, E. D. Holton, H. L. Palmer, I. A. Lapham and Judge Arthur MacArthur.

On Oct. 27, 1856, the council by a unanimous vote donated the lots and the contracts for the buildings were let. The

St. Mary's Hospital is the building in
the foreground of this 1906 photo,
taken just four years before the
structure was razed. St. Rose
Orphanage, also organized by the
Daughters of Charity, stands in the
background.

The Better Angels of Human Nature

1910–1958

WITH THE COMPLETION of the new hospital building in early 1910, St. Mary's entered the twentieth century with a renewed vote of confidence from its many supporters and with the unwavering dedication of its nursing and medical staff. The enrollment in the nursing school continued its steady growth, and the early decades of the twentieth century brought many more breakthroughs in medicine that enhanced the ability of doctors and hospitals to cure patients, perform successful surgeries, and add to the overall health of their environments.

Milwaukee had come out of its dark ages of disease and epidemic, and under the new health-conscious leadership of the Socialist mayors, it began to win national awards as the "healthiest city in the nation." The only exception was the onset of the disastrous flu epidemic of 1918, which challenged health care institutions around the world with its deadly onslaught.

The New Hospital Becomes a Reality

Managing hospital finances had become a more challenging task with the growth of many specializations and the need for increasingly sophisticated instruments and drugs after 1900. At the dawn of the twentieth century, lay nurses made between $2 and $16 a month at St. Mary's, and teachers at the nursing school made up to $20 a month. Orderlies made between $8 and $39 a month, and horse-driven ambulance drivers cleared $40 a month, more than twice as much as nurses. The Daughters earned only a small allowance and room and board.

However, even with the unpaid labor of the Daughters, it was hard to make ends meet. With a yearly cost averaging $8,000 to run the hospital, the annual deficit was often more than $1,000. Appeals to the state legislature to contribute more were not answered, due in part to a rising opposition in political circles to subsidies for private institutions out of the public treasury.

However, one ardent supporter of the hospital, a newspaper editor from Racine, wrote that "among these institutions, one is most holy…we have so characterized it in the halls of the legislature. We allude to the Daughters of Charity [upon which] our legislature turns a deaf ear, [although] the institution itself never turns a deaf ear on those who ask for aid, no matter what the creed, color, or condition of the applicant."

This appeal, among others, helped achieve the passage of a bill that subsidized St. Mary's and several other institutions for their care of the public, with a stipend of $500 annually.

Undaunted by the rising costs of operating the hospital, its able administrator, Sister Dolores Gillespie,

Construction crews line up for this 1909 photo of the nearly completed St. Mary's Hospital. The new, half-million-dollar facility was designed to hold 200 beds.

undertook a massive fund-raising effort beginning just after the turn of the century. Her goal was nothing less than funding for an entirely new hospital building to replace the old one and bring St. Mary's fully into the twentieth century.

Another Cornerstone

On Sunday, May 9, 1909, the cornerstone was laid for the new St. Mary's Hospital. More than a thousand people attended the ceremony, and Judge James G. Jenkins made the principal address. Buried with the stone were liturgical documents, coins, newspapers, several holy medals, a Rosary, and a picture of Mother Seton. Several clergymen presided over the blessing, and the Marquette College Glee Club sang. Urging the populace to support the work of the Daughters and contribute to the building fund, Judge Jenkins noted:

It is a hopeful sign, in this age of the almighty dollar, when men become frenzied in a wild struggle for wealth, that institutions can be maintained and conducted upon strictly business principles, based upon the highest motives—to minister to the suffering of man and to care for the sick, the injured, and the dying. It proves that the better angels of human nature are not wholly silenced.

In response to Jenkins' appeal, the number of volunteers increased at the hospital, working to aid the Daughters and to help in fund-raising efforts. On November 21, 1909, fifty women met at the hospital and decided to form an aid society. It was incorporated in April of the following year under the name of the Woman's Auxiliary Guild,

St. Mary's Hospital, Milwaukee, Wisconsin. The members of the guild knitted garments for the sick, furnished and renovated rooms, and raised funds. They would be much needed in the coming decade, which would bring to St. Mary's the victims of the First World War and the flu epidemic of 1918.

The patients of St. Mary's were moved into the new building on June 28, 1910. Sister Alphonsus Porter, pharmacist from 1909 to 1938, remembered the big day:

The old building, erected in 1857 near the Northpoint water tower, was torn down soon thereafter, having served the sick of the greater Milwaukee community for more than 50 years.

The Birth of Modern Surgery

At the dawn of the twentieth century, the technology of the instruments used by surgeons began a steady improvement. A hospital order for surgical implements, placed with the Sharp & Smith Company of Chicago, listed not just surgical tools but also artificial

The new facility boasted the same beautiful views of Lake Michigan that patients of the old building enjoyed, as well as entrances from North and Lake drives. This view from Lake Drive shows the nearly completed building.

Everything began to move with a wonderful rapidity. As the work began I watched their nimble feet running like marathon racers and my heart sank within me and I had visions of broken bottles and a general mix-up.

To my great relief everything was in a short time carried to safety…With the temperature 90 degrees in the shade, moving was to say the least a hot process.

When Judge James G. Jenkins made the principal address at the laying of the cornerstone for the new St. Mary's Hospital in 1909, he was a prominent man in the Milwaukee community. Judge Jenkins had been a resident of Milwaukee since 1857, serving as city attorney and federal district judge before retiring in 1905. Courtesy, Milwaukee County Historical Society

pressure this schedule placed upon them during moving day:

> *Several surgeons wishing to be the first to perform operations in the new St. Mary's [had] many operations scheduled for June 29 and Sister Catherine had to step lively, for Surgeons do not brook, or excuse delays.*

Across the country, techniques in performing surgery were improving at a rapid rate. The use of intubation of the larynx to help diphtheria patients had been developed before the turn of the century, as had the ability to perform safer appendectomies. Following the establishment of the Mayo Clinic in Rochester, Minnesota, in 1889, there were many advances in preventing surgical shock, the leading cause of fatality among surgery patients. In addition to those who entered hospitals for dangerous and difficult surgeries, there were many who increasingly used the facilities for minor injuries as well.

St. Mary's 90 patients were moved to the new hospital building on June 28, 1910. While the Daughters walked through the corridors admiring their new surroundings, a few things were still under construction—including the kitchen. It had not yet been completed by the day of the move, forcing Sister Gertrude Dooling to cook for the entire hospital population over the next year on what she called "a little old gas stove."

limbs, artificial eyes, and crutches.

With refinements in anesthesiology and with better training for surgeons at the new medical college, surgery became an increasingly sophisticated branch of medical care with its own highly precise rules and procedures, which also demanded the growth of special training for surgical nurses. The day after the move into the new building, the staff surgeons had scheduled several operations in order to be the first to use the state-of-the-art facilities in the new operating room. One Daughter recalled the tremendous

Outpatient Services
Technology was changing quickly, and these changes touched every part of the hospital. With the rise of mass transit, and even the sales of a few automobiles before the war, people became much more mobile. The realization that a

This receipt is for a donation to the Woman's Auxiliary Guild, established in 1909. Members were cited in 1914 for replacing the hospital's flagstaff (the original was destroyed by lightning) and furnishing the dispensary with equipment and instruments and defraying expenses of several operations.

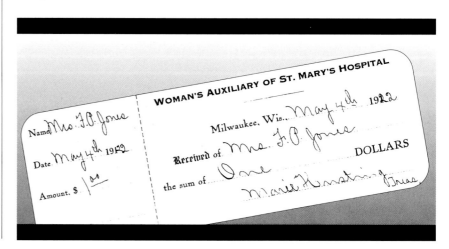

number of patients could leave work or home to reside at the hospital for a short stay led to the construction of an outpatient department at St. Mary's, opened on April 1, 1912.

The department had its own surgical, sterilizing, and dressing rooms, and 208 people were treated there in its first seven months of operation.

Dr. W.C.F. Witte, a surgeon on the staff, donated the equipment for an emergency pathological laboratory in 1914. With the fully equipped X-ray department and an early, albeit still primitive, pathology laboratory, diagnosis could be accomplished with much more speed and treatment decided accordingly.

Wisconsin Wrecking Company is shown in this circa 1910 photo handling the demolition of the original St. Mary's Hospital building, which was condemned and had become too costly to repair. Original plans to add a north wing were scrapped in favor of constructing a brand-new facility.

In 1914 surgeon W.C.F. Witte made a donation allowing for the establishment of an emergency pathological laboratory in the surgical department. Witte served as chief of staff at St. Mary's from 1922 to 1926.

Right: In September 1912 St. Mary's Training School for Nurses was incorporated. The school was accredited by the Wisconsin State Board of Health the following year.

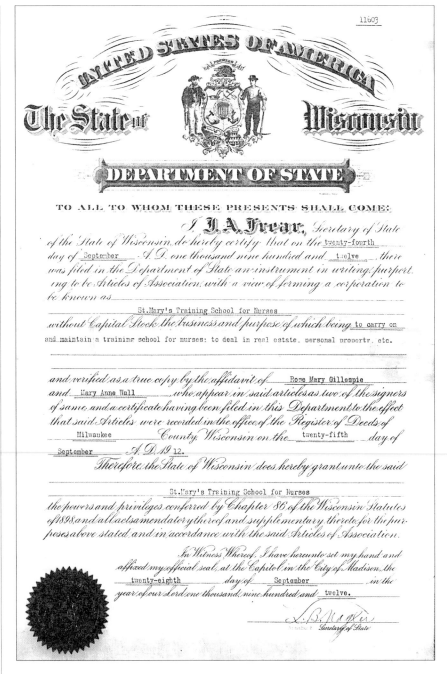

Higher State Requirements for Staff

Standards for the training of all medical caregivers, both physicians and nurses, were raised by the state in the early twentieth century. The St. Mary's Training School for Nurses became incorporated on September 16, 1912, and the Wisconsin State Board of Health approved the accreditation of the school through September 1915, when it was transferred to the Wisconsin State Board of Medical Examiners.

In addition, a state law went into effect on September 1, 1914, that required examinations for all "registered" nurses. By 1917 nurses admitted to the school had to present proof of high school attendance. Interestingly, the not-yet-standardized Wisconsin "medical schools" of the time had no such requirement. These came somewhat later. Medical education for doctors in Wisconsin had a dismal history, with many commercial attempts being so badly operated that they were described by an examiner as "utterly wretched, without a redeeming feature."

The trustees of Marquette University purchased one failing commercial school in 1913, and opened the Marquette University School of Medicine. The University of Wisconsin-Madison did not begin to offer medical studies until 1907, and a full four-year medical program in 1919, after the war.

Pharmacy regulations were becoming more stringent as well. In January 1912, Sister Alphonsus received word that she was required to take the state board examinations in pharmacy. Sister wryly remarked later that it was "the shock of her life, and perhaps her heart trouble and high blood pressure may be traced back to this date." The quarterly deadline for registration had passed but Sister traveled to Madison in April and passed all three of the required tests.

Mortar and Pestle

The pharmacy at the early part of the century would be unrecognizable today. It was a small room, enclosed by a porch with glass windows. There was one glass case containing glass labeled bottles. A very small stock of medicine on hand consisted of powdered drugs, tinctures, fluid extracts, and two or three packages of "biological serums." Vitamins and ampoules were unknown at this time, as was intravenous glucose. A book contained recipes for "whooping cough mixture," "inebriate mixture," "blackberry cordial," "certain cure for cancer," and other tonics. The drug companies did not deliver their wares, so empty cans and jugs for refilling had to be ready when the

Daughters took the horse and carriage to market.

As with medical knowledge and techniques, however, research in the science of drugs was making great strides in the early decades of the twentieth century. The discovery in 1914 of Vitamin A and in 1916 of Vitamin B was followed by the isola-

tion of Vitamins C, D, and E before 1932. In 1941 Vitamin B was shown to be a complex of at least five distinct vitamins, and the uses of vitamins in the prevention and treatment of disease advanced rapidly.

The greatest breakthrough in drugs, of course, occurred during the 1930s with the discovery of sulfa drugs by researchers in Germany, France, and at Johns Hopkins Medical School in Baltimore. Soon several sulfa derivatives were used effectively to treat diseases from scarlet fever to tonsillitis, peritonitis, blood poisoning, and impetigo.

Beginning in 1939, the discovery of the tremendous potential of antibiotics began with research at the Rockefeller Institute in New York, where tyrothricin was isolated. The development of penicillin, by a London scien-

St. Mary's 66th annual report, compiled for the year ending November 30, 1914, featured a montage of pictures and descriptions of the hospital's interior, which was just a few years old. Hospital room rates ranged from $8 a week (general ward) to $10 (private ward). Maternity cases and patients wanting private rooms were charged as much as $20 a week and sometimes more.

tist in 1941, and its transfer to the United States was followed by a multitude of other antibiotic agents in the next several decades. The miracle of modern pharmaceuticals had begun.

However, even with the growing ability to treat diseases with drugs, the importance of good nutrition and a sterile environment continued to be top priorities at the hospital.

Keeping the House of God

Sister Gertrude Dooling was in charge of housekeeping, and possessed other talents as well. A marvel of economy, she canned and preserved fruits and vegetables as they came into season. She made all the soap that was used in the kitchen, and still had some to spare for dishwashing

in other departments.

Purchasing, cooking, and preserving food became more than a full-time job for the growing kitchen staff after the turn of the century. Soon the specialties of meal planning, nutrition consulting, and dietetics would add many members to the hospital staff. During the 1920s and thereafter, research into hormone and endocrine therapy resulted in the isolation of both adrenaline and the much-valued insulin. The treatment of diabetes became possible, and the hospital staff came to realize that careful nutritional planning, as well as pharmaceutical treatments, was a significant part of medical care. By the early twentieth century the advance of motorized transportation,

This horse-drawn carriage served as St. Mary's first ambulance. The hospital's telephone number—Lake 79—is indicated on the side. A notation on the back of the original photograph lists the carriage price at $600, f.o.b. Photo by Charles Abrecsh Co.

along with breakthroughs in refrigeration, resulted in the greater availability of many vegetables and fruits year-round.

Preparing for the Horseless Carriage

Between 1913 and 1940 residents of Milwaukee, like elsewhere across the country, became accustomed to buying and driving automobiles. From one car for every 103 citizens in 1913, the percentage of ownership increased by 1940 to one for every four people in the city. This new technology, along with the telephone, changed patterns of hospital usage and placed new demands upon the staff for service.

One advertisement for an automobile in the *Wisconsin Medical Journal* featured a photograph of a Model K Cadillac, with the descriptive phrase, "Doctor's Delight… More of these cars are used by doctors than all other makes of cars in Milwaukee." Even though the average patient could not afford the car's $750 pricetag, the rise of automobile ownership and the use of telephones meant

that the availability of medical resources was at one's fingertips. A motorized ambulance was just a phone call away. All of the new drugs and new technology meant that the average life expectancy for a Wisconsinite by 1930 was 11 years longer than it had been in 1915, an astonishing gain in a very short time.

The hospital did not purchase its first automobile until 1923. Transportation for the Daughters until then consisted of a covered wagon, known as Old Maria, pulled by an ancient horse named Dolly. (A local carriage company held a contract for the horse-driven ambulance.) Dolly moved slowly and stumbled often.

The hospital pharmacy was described in the 1914 annual report as being "equipped with the latest appurtenances (equipment & instruments) and fully stocked."

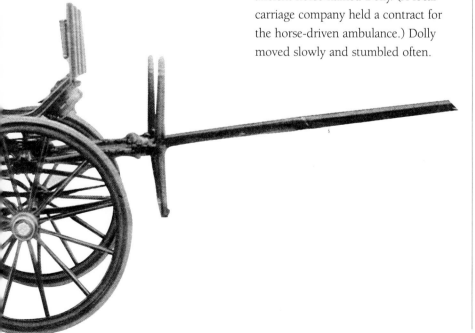

After World War I began, St. Mary's staff cared for many servicemen—as many as 85 a month by 1920. Soldiers head off to war from the Milwaukee Road Depot in this photo, circa 1917. Courtesy, Milwaukee County Historical Society

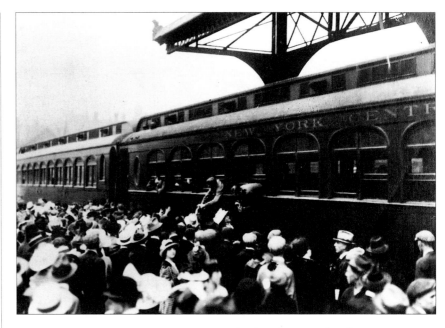

Passing trains, however, would rouse her to "kick up her heels and almost upset Maria."

Milwaukee also developed a motorized bus system, along with its rail mass transit. During the 1920s automobile traffic began to crowd the streets of the city, and hospitals had to plan for parking lots, along with paved circle driveways. One tourist bus driver, a great friend of the Daughters, loved to take his passengers around the city and include the new St. Mary's Hospital on his tour of the east side. According to one account, the Daughters felt great pride each time they heard the driver of the tourist bus call out, "This is St. Mary's Hospital, the finest hospital in the Northwest."

The Great War

The First World War greatly increased the number of sailors and soldiers cared for at St. Mary's. Although the United States did not officially enter World War I until 1917, three years after it began, a military draft was in effect throughout the decade. Many servicemen contracted illnesses at army and naval bases, and then had to be sent back to civilian hospitals. During

the first five months of American involvement in World War I, the Daughters at St. Mary's nursed 239 soldiers. As late as June 1920, well after the armistice, the hospital was

still providing medical care for about 85 soldiers a month.

The hospital staff contributed to the war effort in other ways as well. The hospital purchased $2,000 worth of war bonds, and donated money to other local drives. Eventually 45 graduates of St. Mary's Training School for Nurses volunteered for and served the military during the war, as did two interns and 10 of the doctors on staff. Sister Dolores Gillespie proudly wrote, referring to these alumni, "Our Flag counted fifty-seven stars."

The hospital also served as a de facto rehabilitation center for returning veterans. The Knights of Columbus were constant visitors at St. Mary's, and provided a vocational teacher and weekly movies for the convalescents. At Christmas a tree, music, and gifts of candy and ciga-rettes were provided for hospital residents by the Knights as well.

The Worst Epidemic

The flu epidemic of 1918, which came on the heels of the First World War, first reached Milwaukee in the fall, with subsequent waves of the illness affecting the population over the next two years. It was the worst epidemic in recorded history, and it is estimated that the flu killed 10 times more people than the war itself—some 500,000 people in the United States alone, and 20 million worldwide.

This influenza affected the respiratory system and often quickly developed into fatal pneumonia. During the worst part of the epidemic, the city closed schools, churches, theaters, and libraries. Politicians ceased campaigning for the fall elections and many

Forty-five graduates from St. Mary's Training School for Nurses served in the army and navy during World War I. Nurses cared for troops in America and also on the fronts of France, England, and Belgium. Members of the army nurses' corps, including 1917 graduate Jean Tramontine (front row, third from left), pose for this 1918 photo at Jefferson Barracks, Missouri.

On August 27, 1927, ground was broken for Seton Hall, the new residence for the School of Nursing. Sister Dolores Gillespie (holding shovel), hospital administrator from 1904 to 1927, officiated at the ceremony.

public events were canceled as people stayed home to avoid exposure to the virus. One theory held that chewing Horlick's malted milk tablets (made in Racine) would increase a person's resistance to the disease. Physicians prescribed bed rest and castor oil, but none of these remedies helped.

St. Mary's was the first hospital in the city to admit the contagious victims. Cots had to be placed in the corridors and sun porches to accommodate the large numbers of patients. Sister Dolores wrote about its horrible dimensions on October 6, 1918:

The onset of the disease was very rapid, if the lungs were involved, [the victims] immediately became cyanotic [turned blue from poorly oxygenated blood] and lasted but a few days.

The influenza moved so quickly and was so highly contagious that a number of the Daughters caught it, unlike the earlier epidemics of smallpox, diphtheria, or cholera, which they had been fortunate enough to avoid. One journal noted, "Three of our nurses at the Great Lakes Naval Station had it, and have recovered." However, only one week later, in November 1918, six more Daughters became ill, one

hospital and the city settled down to the postwar era, looking ahead to the 1920s with optimism.

By 1920 the city had recovered from the ravages of the flu and the Socialist leadership had instituted many health care reforms that soon brought Milwaukee recognition as one of the "healthiest cities in the nation." The death rate had fallen to 11.6 per 100, from an earlier rate of almost twice that, 18.33, just 30 years before.

with pneumonia, several tragically died, and the hospital was closed to most visitors.

The senior Daughter asked for additional help, but every medical institution across the country was in similar dire circumstances and no additional help could be sent to Milwaukee. She decided to pray and wrote briefly, "We must trust in God."

In addition to the hospital patients and sailors, the Daughters also helped nurse more than 100 children from St. Rose Orphanage who contracted the flu. With the constant care of the nursing staff, many of the children recovered. When the worst ravages of the epidemic passed by late 1919, the

Regulations of dairies for pure milk production, the opening of free clinics for inoculations, the completion of the city sewer system, garbage collection, the treatment of city water, and the tuberculin testing of cattle were just a few of the measures that produced these results.

Prohibition

Part of the reform movement of the early twentieth century that had brought the income tax, the Federal Reserve System for banking, and the women's vote before 1920 was the movement to reduce American consumption of intoxicating beverages, the Temperance Movement. The passage of the Eighteenth Amendment to the U.S.

Seton Hall, later named Grueninger Hall, became the new home for St. Mary's School of Nursing in November 1928. The building housed classrooms and more than doubled the dormitory facilities for students. Today it is the site of St. Mary's Medical Clinic-Northpoint.

Constitution in 1920, which prohibited the manufacture, sale, or transportation of intoxicating liquors, created another challenge for the hospital.

Like all medical institutions, St. Mary's made use of "non-beverage alcohol" for medicinal purposes, and thus had to pay a special fee of $1,000 to the federal government for legal permission to do so. The repeal of this amendment in 1933 did nothing to lower taxes on alcohol. In 1934 the hospital had to pay $3,300 to the government for the use of Tax Free Alcohol.

The Owl's Nest and Seton Hall

It was clear by the beginning of the 1920s that the quarters for student nurses were inadequate and new

As shown in this 1940s photo, students from St. Rose Orphanage participated in the May Queen procession held each year to honor the Blessed Virgin Mary.

These hospital interns, at St. Mary's from 1929 to 1930, helped care for the rising number of patients. In 1930 the annual entry of patients was 6,311. Just five years before, the annual patient census was listed at 4,977. Back row (left to right): Dr. Ross, Dr. Jerome W. Fons, Sr., and Dr. Wilfried Seng. Front row (left to right): Dr. Dodson, Dr. William Studley, and Dr. Sylvester Darling.

options were discussed. A brick home at the north end of the hospital property was purchased in 1924, and 24 nurses moved into it. Affectionately known as "The Owl's Nest," this house was only a temporary solution to the problem. With the rising enrollment at the nursing school and the growing demand for nurses at the hospital, the decision was soon made to build an entirely new dormitory.

Ground was broken for a new nurses' home, and on November 21, 1928, Seton Hall—named in honor of Elizabeth Bayley Seton, the founder of the American Daughters of Charity—was formally opened. The student nurses enjoyed dances in the gym, but the rules were strict. Students could be "campused" (grounded) for such infractions as having a uniform and apron of unequal length, being late for breakfast, or having two rows of curls instead of one.

A 1934 graduate of the nursing program remembered being forbidden to wear lipstick "until all of the male patients rebelled and offered to give up their beds to us as we looked sicker than they." Despite the plea of the male patients, the rule against lipstick continued through the 1940s, and smoking was grounds for dismissal from the school. It was made clear to the nursing students and the entire staff that professional standards of behavior were expected from everyone.

The Great Depression

Following the Stock Market Crash in 1929, the onset of the Great Depression brought the problems of massive unemployment across the country. In Milwaukee, the jobless rate passed 30 percent and, as a result, fewer people could afford to eat well, hunger increased, diseases spread, and the growing number of poor could not afford medical care.

The problems of the Depression affected St. Mary's

The Great Depression brought ever-increasing numbers of charity cases through St. Mary's doors. The Daughters continued to provide health care, home visits, and food and clothing to the needy during this busy time. Courtesy, Medical Society of Milwaukee County

St. Mary's operating rooms formerly were located on the fifth floor of what is now the east facility. The operating room in this circa 1955 photo afforded the St. Mary's surgical team a view of St. Rose Orphanage, located on the west side of the hospital, as well as views of the surrounding area.

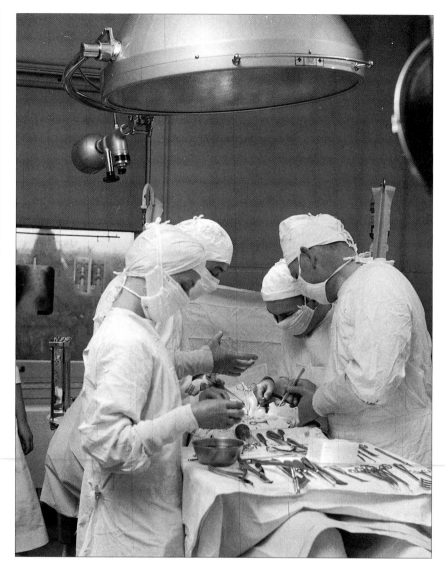

in a variety of ways. Statistics show that in the state of Wisconsin at this time, income from patients fell while the number of charity cases quadrupled.

The hospital was not only providing health care for the needy, including home visits, but food and clothing as well. From 1930 through 1933 hundreds of people received warm dinners daily. One nursing student remembered being fed bread and butter and syrup to fill the gaps in the menus. However, the combination of a devoted lay staff, the unpaid labor of the Daughters of Charity, and the bequests of wealthy patients and companies kept the hospital financially afloat throughout the hard times.

While hospital usage actually declined during some years of the Depression, the need for crisis care continued to escalate.

A Burning Tragedy and the Treatment of Burns

A large explosion at the Krause Milling Company on April 13, 1937, sent 13 of 30 injured men to St. Mary's Hospital. Newspaper accounts do not relate the complete outcome of the disaster but at least seven died, one at St. Mary's. Most of the victims were badly burned, and required several caretakers each. An account of that time states: "Time and food

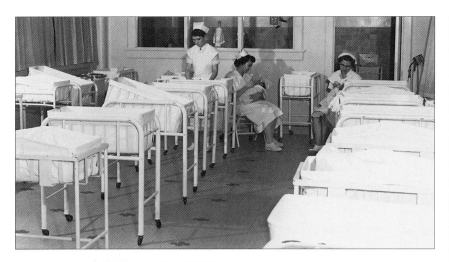

St. Mary's maternity ward had grown over the years to accommodate the ever-growing number of infants. By 1927 the nursery had been expanded and a second delivery room was planned. A new nursery was added in 1942, and by the 1950s some 200 babies were being delivered at St. Mary's each year.

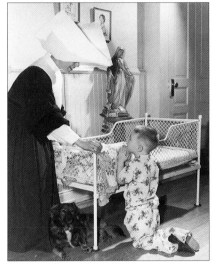

whereby people could buy a form of health insurance, through prepayment into a fund. In 1939 the Blue Cross insurance plan came to Wisconsin, and that same year St. Mary's contracted with its "Plan for Hospital Insurance."

During the next several decades many hospitals around the country would join a Blue Cross, or other, health insurance plan. These insurance programs benefited hospitals with a steadier flow of income, as well as patients, who were assured some

The Daughters established St. Vincent's Infant Asylum to provide a haven for unwed mothers and their infants, as well as orphaned babies. The asylum, which officially opened on Milwaukee's south side in 1877, housed infants and children under five years of age—as seen in this circa 1950s photograph. If the youngsters were still at St. Vincent's when they reached the age of five years, boys were usually sent to St. Aemilian's and girls to St. Rose Orphanage. St. Vincent's Infant Asylum closed in October 1958.

meant nothing. Many remained up all night to care for the men."

The treatment of burns, as well as the emergency care provided to victims of automobile accidents, demanded an entirely new approach to dealing with open flesh wounds, which were dangerously vulnerable to infection. It also demanded new breakthroughs in pain control, which the next several decades would bring as St. Mary's became a pioneering institution in the treatment of such catastrophic burns before 1960.

Into the 1940s

As the country climbed out of the Depression, St. Mary's financial picture also improved. Beginning in Texas, several hospitals had devised a plan

St. Mary's School of Nursing graduate Jane Siefert, shown here in uniform in 1943, was among the 100 St. Mary's nurses who served in World War II and the Korean Conflict.

Shortly after St. Mary's Hospital Guild was founded in 1952, appeals for funding were started to help pay for the new north wing. The addition was needed to house new equipment and to accommodate the growing numbers of patients.

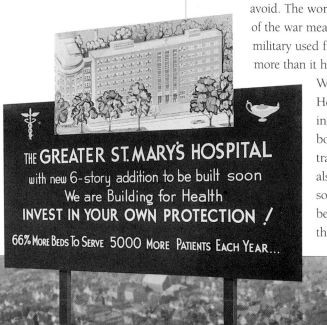

form of protection from devastating medical costs arising from a health care crisis.

Another World War

The bombing of Pearl Harbor on December 7, 1941, brought America into a war it had tried mightily to avoid. The worldwide scope of the war meant that the military used field hospitals more than it had in the First World War. However, the increased use of both air and rail transportation also meant that soldiers could be returned to their home-

towns more rapidly for treatment and recovery.

There was a shortage of nurses on the homefront because many women signed up to help at the military hospitals around the world. More than 100 graduates of St. Mary's School of Nursing served with the armed forces. Catherine M. Kain, an alumna who had also been educational director at the school, was a lieutenant commander in the naval reserves and eventually became commander of the nurses' corps. Nineteen nurses also completed cadet training in various government hospitals.

The Impact of the Baby Boom

The growing number of births in the postwar baby boom brought the need for expanded maternity care to hospi-

tals. The practice of delivering babies at home had almost vanished from medical charts by war's end. Whereas 62 percent of babies were born at home in 1930, the number declined to only one percent by 1950. Hospitals had to prepare for this vast new influx of patients into maternity wards. During the 1950s more than 200 babies were born at

passed a national survey with flying colors, being listed among the first to be granted accreditation by the National League of Nursing Education. Federal funds helped keep the enrollment of nurses up during the war, but at war's end the declining enrollments became a serious problem.

In 1947 a Nursing Advisory

Facing, bottom: *The hospital site, originally selected because of its remote location, had undergone tremendous growth and development since the turn of the century. This early 1950s aerial photograph shows St. Mary's Hospital and the School of Nursing. Photo by Lee Fray Studios*

St. Mary's each year.

The ever-increasing patient population also made plans for a new pediatric unit necessary. Childhood mortality rates had fallen dramatically during the first five decades of the twentieth century, as the use of new drugs curtailed killers like diphtheria, scarlet fever, tuberculosis, and typhoid. In 1943 the average baby could expect to live at least 10 years longer than one born in 1918, and the rate continued to climb.

Unfortunately, the postwar years brought a nationwide decrease in the number of people enrolled in nursing schools and the general shortage of nurses became an increasing problem. In 1940 St. Mary's nursing school

Committee was appointed to oversee changes in curriculum and instruction at the school and to try to increase enrollment. They recommended several changes to dormitory and student rules that included permission to marry during the final year, and permission to live off campus. In later years the nursing school allied with other educational institutions to keep its program viable for as long as possible.

Centennial Years

The 100th anniversary of the opening of St. Mary's was celebrated from 1946 through 1948. A book, *The Daughters of Charity in Milwaukee 1846-1946*, by the Reverend Peter Leo Johnson, was commissioned and published. On

The Daughters of Charity not only were busy performing hospital duties, they also served as instructors at St. Mary's School of Nursing and St. Rose Orphanage. Some of the sisters gathered for this 1954 photo when the School of Nursing celebrated its 60-year anniversary. Seated (left to right): Sisters Josephine, Frances, Rose Maguire (hospital administrator, 1942-1954), Hermine Regan (hospital administrator, 1954-1960), and Leo. Standing (left to right): Sisters Rosaria, Marciana, Catherine, Estelle, and Isidore.

October 29, 1946, solemn Mass was celebrated at St. John's Cathedral. Archbishop Moses E. Kiley presided, and numerous other clergy attended and assisted. A pageant was held that evening, featuring choral selections and dramatizations of important chapters of St. Mary's history.

One of the hallmarks of the hospital's first 100 years had always been the widespread community support it had received. The centennial marked a time for many to renew their commitment and to join a variety of groups organized to improve that support.

Help from the Laity and Plans for Growth

Building on the earlier work of the volunteers in the Woman's Auxiliary Guild, St. Mary's Hospital Guild was founded by eight members in 1952, with Catherine M. Hormuth serving as its first president. The following year, a lay

advisory board was formed with members of the business community and plans were made for a new north wing, as well as an appeal for funding. The hospital had to complete a new power plant within the facility in order to accommodate new electronic equipment and rewiring throughout the building. The building fund plan called for an increase of bed capacity from 190 to 315. Cash and pledges eventually amounted to more than $1.5 million as the excitement of adding many new features in the new wing escalated.

Planning for the Postwar Years

St. Mary's Hospital during the 1950s was operating at between 95 and 100 percent capacity. It admitted more than 10,000 people annually. The number of X-rays and laboratory tests

Sister Hermine Regan, hospital administrator from 1954 to 1960, and Dr. Dexter Witte watch as Dr. Ervin Bernhardt breaks ground at the site of the hospital's new north wing on March 17, 1957. Both Bernhardt and Witte served terms as president of St. Mary's medical staff.

A Daughter of Charity in the older-style habit descends the grand staircase located in the lobby of St. Mary's Hospital (now the east facility) in this 1955 photo. The hospital was operating at a nearly full capacity, prompting talk of building a new wing to accommodate the growing needs of the community.

Standing on the site of the original St. Mary's Hospital, the nearly completed north wing (seen here in February 1958) stood six stories high and boasted spectacular views of the lake. Photo by Woerfel Corporation

had doubled since the 1940s, and the "new" 1908 building began to seem outdated and very overcrowded. With more than 50 nursing graduates serving on active duty during the Korean Conflict, the demands for better training and better educational facilities for nurses also increased.

The ground was broken for the new north wing—now known as the Hill Building—on March 17, 1957. The actual work on the new wing began on June 9 and would usher in yet another new era in the history of St. Mary's Hospital. The 1950s proved to be a watershed decade in the history of American medical care and set the stage for many exciting changes as St. Mary's stayed abreast of these changes and led the way in specific new fields of treatment.

Carrying the Legacy Forward

1958–1976

A S MILWAUKEE entered the 1960s St. Mary's Hospital was able to continue its legacy of service, building upon traditions dating back to the time of St. Louise de Marillac and St. Vincent de Paul. However, the hospital was also able to blend this mission of service with the energy and foresight necessary to remain on the cutting edge of the rapidly emerging field of modern medicine. Its contributions in the treatment of burn victims during the 1960s proved so outstanding that the hospital became recognized as one of the leading burn centers in the country.

Expansion in the 1960s

The dedication of the new north wing of St. Mary's Hospital on June 6, 1959, was marked with a grand ceremony. Numerous luminaries of the Daughters of Charity and the archdiocese spoke, and the cornerstone was set by the Most Reverend William E. Cousins, archbishop of Milwaukee. Many lay people were in attendance as well. The popular mayor, Frank P. Zeidler, came to celebrate this addition to the city's oldest

hospital, as did the 32nd Infantry Division of the Wisconsin Army National Guard, in full dress regalia to honor the home of so many of their fellow soldiers over the decades.

The Beginnings of the Burn Center

St. Mary's was about to break another type of medical ground.

In 1957 staff surgeon Dr. John Klein was called in to assess the burn victims of an electrical accident at the Wisconsin Electric Power Company Oak Creek Power Plant. During the 1950s burn patients were treated at whatever hospital happened to be closest to the accident by staff with varying degrees of experience in this field. Klein saw the need for a specialized burn treatment center in a facility staffed by skilled and more experienced personnel.

Working with the Daughters at St. Mary's, Klein was able to convince the Wisconsin Electric Power Company (WEPCO) of the importance of such a place, and received assurance of financial support. He then visited some of the few existing burn centers in the country and brought this gathered expertise back to establish a state-of-the-art burn center at St. Mary's. The burn center would become the fourth of its kind in the United States.

Klein's plan called for a staff of surgeons trained in burn care, as well as several plastic surgeons. The nurses in the new section volunteered to work there, and Dr. George Collentine, who was soon appointed the medical director of the burn center, called them "the unit's first true heroines and heroes." Collentine later recalled how the unit involved nurses in decision making, which was in marked contrast to the traditional boss/helper relationship of doctor and nurse:

In the 1959 annual report, eight physicians were recognized for their 50 years of service. Seated (left to right): Drs. A.J. Weber, Theodore Rolfs, and T.A. Judge. Standing (left to right): Dr. E.W. Miller, Dr. H.O. McMahon, and administrator Sister Hermine. (Not pictured: Drs. A.T. Holbrook, J.W. Kleinboehl, and A.F. Rheineck.)

Because we had no house staff, we outlined sets of contingency orders for nurses, the nurses would carry out diagnostic measures and even initiate certain therapeutic measures. This was very unconventional.

The original burn unit had two rooms to house patients, an admitting and dressing room, an alcove with a whirlpool hydrotherapy tub, and a hoist to raise and lower patients. The unit also had a custom air filtration system that provided precise control of

The State Medical Society of Wisconsin erected a historical marker just outside St. Mary's present east facility on September 18, 1966. The marker commemorated the Daughters of Charity and their success in opening St. John's Infirmary, the state's first public hospital.

In June 1959 dignitaries from around the city, including Mayor Frank P. Zeidler, attended the dedication ceremony of St. Mary's new north wing. The addition later became the site of St. Mary's Hill Psychiatric Hospital and presently houses Sacred Heart Rehabilitation Institute.

temperature, humidity, and airborne infectious material. It was, in essence, a highly specialized intensive care unit.

The Electric Company Burn Therapy Center was formally opened on August 19, 1959. On that date, a critically burned stock car driver from Slinger, Wisconsin, was admitted as the first patient. He lived for five days. Several other patients were transferred in from other hospitals in the sur-

rounding area; only six of the first 12 patients survived their injuries. However, with each passing month the science of burn treatment became increasingly sophisticated and important progress was made.

The doctors and the highly skilled staff on the unit continued to learn and advance. Collentine spent time at the country's top burn care facility in San Antonio, Texas, observing the best burn

Dr. George Collentine was medical director of St. Mary's Regional Burn Center for the first 26 years of its existence (1959-1986). He attended and hosted international seminars on burn treatment, and traveled to Paris and Prague to present papers before the International Society for Burn Injuries. Collentine also participated in the founding of the American Burn Association.

Far right: *Dr. Burton Waisbren, internist and infectious disease specialist, worked with Dr. George Collentine, the burn center's first medical director. Waisbren, who assisted in some of the center's pioneering efforts, later served as its associate director. Courtesy, Medical Society of Milwaukee County*

Below: *St. Mary's received widespread recognition when its burn center, one of only four burn units in the United States and the first of its kind in Wisconsin, opened in August 1959. The center has treated thousands of burn victims since then and today it services patients from throughout Wisconsin, northern Illinois, and Michigan's upper peninsula.*

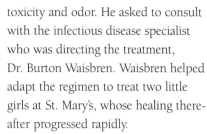

care available in the world at that time. He went over the records of the St. Mary's burn patients with the surgical team in Texas, and was assured that those who did not survive would not have done so elsewhere. He was encouraged to seek out new methods of treatment, especially of the bacterial infections that killed most burn victims.

A breakthrough occurred in 1960, when Collentine observed the progress of two badly burned patients who were being treated at Milwaukee County Hospital with intravenous doses of at least three antibiotics as well as topical antibiotics. Collentine noted that there was an absence of the usual systemic

toxicity and odor. He asked to consult with the infectious disease specialist who was directing the treatment, Dr. Burton Waisbren. Waisbren helped adapt the regimen to treat two little girls at St. Mary's, whose healing thereafter progressed rapidly.

Dr. Waisbren soon became associate director of what is now known as St. Mary's Regional Burn Center. While always fond of Dr. Waisbren, the

Daughters remember the challenges of dealing with his amazing genius. As challenging as the temperaments of some of the specialists might have been, the Daughters recognized the need to exercise patience, in order to learn everything possible about the latest medical breakthroughs. Working together in these specialized treatment centers, the physicians and staff developed a sense of mutual respect and devotion.

Increasing specialization in medicine meant that the day of the general practitioner had almost come to an end. By the late 1950s most staff doctors at hospitals, as well as in the field of medicine overall, were specialists, who had spent years beyond their initial medical training as interns and residents learning one specific area of medicine. Hospitals soon balanced

their staff positions with doctors from each specialized field.

New Departments

With the shortage of nurses in the 1950s and 1960s, the hospital leadership looked at various alternatives to remedy the patient-to-nurse ratio. Just after the war, in 1946, nurses comprised more than 20 percent of the personnel in hospitals, but the number fell to only 12 percent six years later. This percentage decline was balanced somewhat by the fact that by 1952, for every registered nurse, there were two general duty nurses and four auxiliary workers working under her as a team. Still, the shortage of supervisory, fully trained nurses continued to worsen by the 1960s.

One answer was to increase the usage of licensed practical nurses, who took nursing training for two instead of four years, but could perform many of the duties once done by registered nurses alone. A second answer was to allow patients who were not seriously ill to take some responsibility for their own in-house care when possible. St. Mary's Hospital was featured in the May 16, 1960, issue of *Time* magazine in an article called "Do It Yourself Hospital." The hospital had opened an experimental self-care unit for patients who required help at the level between outpatient and intermediate care.

The experimental 25-bed unit required a staff of five, which was one-fourth the usual staff, and it cost the patient far less as well. Double and single rooms cost $14.50 and $16.50 a day in self care, compared to $22.50 and $28 in the rest of the hospital. Despite its popularity with patients, the program was dismantled less than a year later because of a growing patient census and the need

to use the experimental ward for other purposes, including a new urology unit. Nevertheless, the hospital staff and administration had learned many valuable lessons from the experiment that they would apply to staffing needs throughout other units.

Changes in the School of Nursing

As enrollments fell at nursing schools across the country, the cost-effectiveness of housing an entire training program at each hospital was difficult to defend and mergers resulted. In September 1961 St. Mary's School of Nursing entered into an association with Mount Mary College in order to offer students a compromise between three- and four-year nursing programs. St. Mary's nursing students could now earn college credits. As a result, they were faced with a broad spectrum of courses in the liberal arts to choose from, in addition to the science and anatomy courses required for their nursing degree. Moreover, as more traditional college students, they were able to enjoy a greater degree of personal freedom. They were now allowed to marry during their last

Dr. John T. Klein, a staff surgeon for many years at St. Mary's, was instrumental in the development of the burn center after an electrical accident in 1957 sent burn victims to St. Mary's for treatment. After reviewing burn centers in the country and obtaining financial backing from the Wisconsin Electric Power Company, Klein spent more than a year planning and developing the center before it formally opened in August 1959.

St. Mary's School of Nursing underwent several changes in the early 1960s including an association with Mount Mary College. The nursing student in this photo wears the traditional navy blue cape with red lining and criss-cross straps (adopted in 1931-1932) with a "wash-and-wear" short-sleeve uniform (adopted in 1964). This was the last uniform of the school before its closing in 1969.

six months in the program, and to live at home.

It was hoped that the freer nature of the cooperative program with Mount Mary would attract more students into the program, but enrollments continued to be low. St. Mary's still counted on the services of the nurse-trainees who came to do their practice work at the hospital, while finishing their bachelor's degrees. Even after the merger with Mount Mary, the cost of maintaining a nursing program proved too great for the hospital's budget. With the development of a full-scale nursing program at the nearby University of Wisconsin-Milwaukee, the best course seemed to be to close the in-house program that had served the hospital and the Milwaukee community for more than seven decades.

By the mid-1960s private nursing schools across the country were affiliating with public university programs, or closing their doors entirely. A 1957 study had anticipated these changes. Titled *Nurses for A Growing Nation*, the report advocated the greater use of four-year university baccalaureate programs to enhance nursing training and to make it more appealing for both women and men. In addition, the passage of President Kennedy's Nurses Training Act (signed by President Johnson in 1964) brought millions of federal dollars into the support of nursing education.

However, at the same time, the American Nurses' Association published a position paper that declared, "the education for all of those who are licensed to practice nursing should take place in institutions of higher education; minimum preparation for beginning professional nursing practice should be a baccalaureate degree." The day of private, hospital-based nursing programs was waning. Across the country, the total number of nursing programs based in Catholic hospitals declined from 331 in 1966 to only 114 twenty years later.

Despite the city-wide shortage of nurses, it was announced in December 1966 that St. Mary's School of Nursing would close in 1969. Changes in educational requirements and the high cost of maintaining the school were the main reasons for the decision. At that time St. Mary's announced an affiliation with the University of Wisconsin-Milwaukee. The *Milwaukee Journal* published an editorial acknowledging the decision as regrettable but understandable, and called the school "the community's oldest and one of its finest… Its closing…will deprive the community of a valuable teaching resource."

In its 75 years St. Mary's School of Nursing prepared 1,913 graduates for the profession of nursing. Many of its alumnae remained on the staff at St. Mary's, while others have gone on to other forms of nursing, served as military nurses, or joined the staffs at hospitals across Wisconsin.

Ongoing Hospital Renovations

Sister Josephine Atchison came to Milwaukee in 1960 to serve as hospital administrator, just after the dedication of the new north wing, and remained for six years until 1966. Upon her arrival, she noted the symmetry of the 1909 building with its brand-new wing, and the gracious positioning of the hospital at the crest of the lake shore bluff. She was also attracted by the beauty of the city and the views

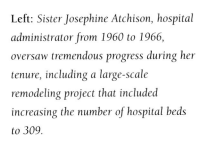

Left: *Sister Josephine Atchison, hospital administrator from 1960 to 1966, oversaw tremendous progress during her tenure, including a large-scale remodeling project that included increasing the number of hospital beds to 309.*

In 1961 St. Mary's Hospital Guild opened a gift shop, "La Cornette," in the new north wing of the hospital. Staffed by guild volunteers for the next 30 years, the shop was eventually relocated to Seton Tower and renamed the Lake Drive Gift Shop.

Radiologists Anthony Grueninger and Young Kim stand next to the radiation therapy equipment that provided treatment to hundreds of patients in the mid-1960s.

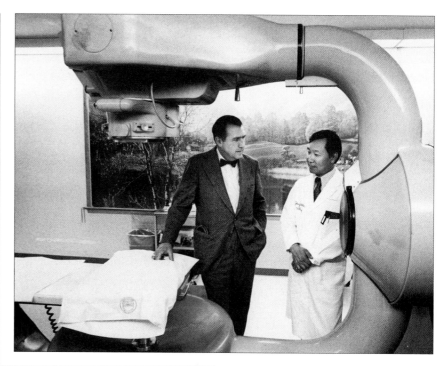

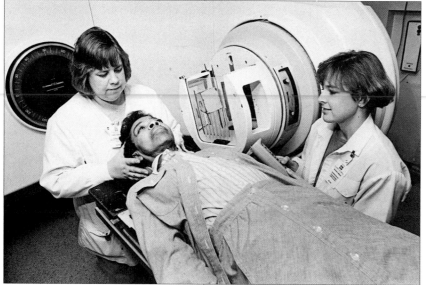

Less than 10 years after St. Mary's opened its cancer center, the hospital received its first linear accelerator to provide radiation therapy to cancer patients. The cobalt unit previously used accommodated about 500 cases a year, while the linear accelerator had the capacity to double that number. The new equipment also provided patients with more precise doses of radiation, thereby decreasing radiation sickness.

from many hospital windows out to Lake Michigan.

During her tenure, an extensive renovation program that included X-ray, emergency rooms, and the laboratory took place.

As the renovations were under way, additional demands upon the staff's expertise remained a constant. On one occasion, a young girl was admitted with a condition in which she was literally starving herself to death. This condition soon became a significant prob-

lem among adolescents, particularly girls, who were obsessively conscious of their physical appearance and denied themselves food to prevent weight gain.

This was the hospital's first case of what became called "anorexia nervosa," soon recognized as a wide-spread problem among teenage girls. The treatment of anorexia demanded personal and family counseling, nutrition work, and occasionally even intravenous feeding. Once again, the changing times called for a quick response to new health problems.

In an effort to deal with this new kind of medical problem, which was often serious enough to be life-threatening, the staff undertook specialized training in the causes, mental complications, and treatment of the new disease. Both the Daughters and the growing number of lay nurses took the lead in the treatment of this illness, a growing and often highly frustrating medical problem.

Radiology and Cancer Treatment

The age of nuclear medicine was dawning, and St. Mary's was a part of it. The

Radiotherapy Department opened its leaded doors in February 1963. The floor had to be rebuilt and reinforced to accommodate the 13,000-pound Cobalt 60 capsule and cancer therapy unit. Radiologist Anthony Grueninger, M.D., called the unit a wonderful "work horse" and the department was administering more than a hundred treatments a day by the mid-1960s. Radiotherapy dealt mostly with cancer, but was also used to treat warts and other skin conditions, bursitis, and arthritis.

The new unit, along with the new Radioisotope—now Nuclear Medicine—Department, and the revamped laboratories, paved the way for the opening of the Cancer Diagnostic and Treatment Center in January 1965. From that year forward, an increasing number of patients sought this form of treatment for problems with a variety of cancers, and the specialization of oncology brought doctors and nurses together in this specialized new effort.

Unlike a century before, when tuberculosis, smallpox, and cholera were the major killers, by the 1960s these three diseases were no longer a threat due to the miracle of antibiotics. However, the new killers were cancer, strokes, and heart disease, all of which demanded new centers within hospitals for diagnosis and treatment.

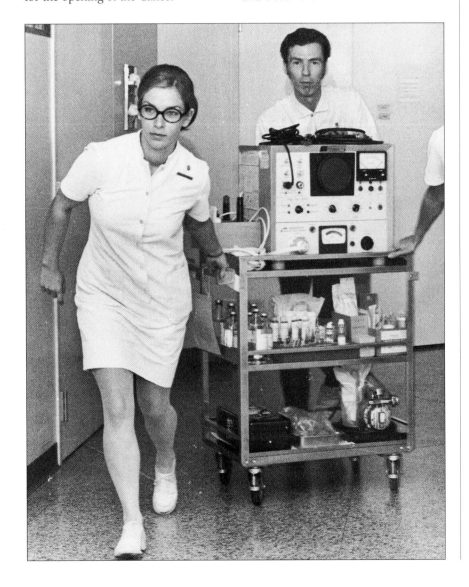

The Cardiac Care Unit (CCU) opened in 1968 and the hospital's first "code team" was established the following year. Code 4 teams, trained to respond immediately to patients needing CPR, were still considered a new concept for hospitals at the time. CCU nurses in this 1969 photo are shown with the hospital's first Code 4 cart as they rush to attend to a patient. The cart housed a monitor with a defibrillator and intravenous medications to treat arrhythmias (irregular heart rhythms). Today the use of Code 4 teams is standard hospital practice.

An innovator in cardiac care, Dr. W. Dudley Johnson performed the world's first coronary bypass operation in 1968. He also perfected the endarterectomy, a technique that involves carefully removing plaque from blocked arteries that are unable to be bypassed. In 1989 Johnson was appointed chairperson of the newly formed Department of Cardiovascular Diseases.

Below: *Cardiac surgeon James Auer checks on a heart surgery patient in this photograph from the early 1970s. Auer helped establish St. Mary's cardiac program by performing the hospital's first coronary bypass operation. Photo by John Kimbal*

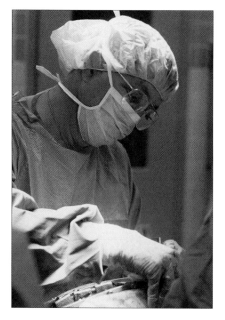

Innovations in Cardiac Care

Over several decades, the life expectancy in Wisconsin had changed dramatically. The doctors at St. Mary's Hospital recognized a need to provide complete care for heart patients. On June 3, 1968, the first coronary care unit opened, under the direction of Dr. George Walcott. The following year the hospital's first surgical intensive care unit was established.

Cardiologist Mukhtar Gani, a specialist in the field of cardiac catheterization, brought his expertise when he joined the staff at St. Mary's in 1970. Once the Cardiac Catheterization Laboratory was established, other developments soon followed. Dr. Gani valued the complete cooperation and support he was given by the hospital administration. As he described it, Sister Julianna Kelly, the administrator, "gave us complete authority to do what we felt was needed. Without her utmost support the heart program would have been impossible."

Dr. John Haugh, the chair of St. Mary's Surgery Department at that time, worked closely with Gani and his team to develop the new unit and was credited for his "wisdom and direction." Haugh was not only a skilled physician, he was also devoutly religious and loved to sing. He became a vital part of the community, beloved by many. One of the Daughters' favorite memories is

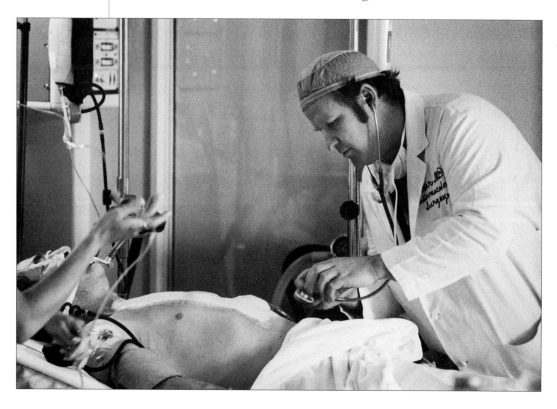

TODD WEHR DIAGNOSTIC CENTER

1848 A M 1973
Serving the community for 125 years

ST MARY'S HOSPITAL
DAUGHTERS of CHARITY of SAINT VINCENT de PAUL

BERTRAND GOLDBERG ASSOCIATES
ARCHITECTS · ENGINEERS

J.A. JONES CONSTRUCTION COMPANY
CONSTRUCTION MANAGEMENT

In 1973 St. Mary's celebrated its 125th anniversary (as shown on Milwaukee's City Hall tower) and was embarking on changes for the future. Planning and construction were already under way for the Northpoint Health Complex, which today includes the patient tower, the Todd Wehr Diagnostic Center, and Seton Tower.

Haugh singing with the assembled hospital community at midnight Mass.

The first coronary bypass at St. Mary's was performed in October 1971 by cardiac surgeon James Auer, M.D., who was assisted by Dr. Haugh and Dr. Tom O'Connor. (Twenty years later the patient was still walking the Capitol Court shopping mall three times a week.) The St. Mary's Cardiac Program had begun.

The world's first coronary bypass operation was performed by Dr. W. Dudley Johnson, a Milwaukee area physician, in 1968. He eventually performed the world's first double, triple, quadruple, and

quintuple bypass surgeries as well. In 1968 Johnson performed Wisconsin's first heart transplant. In 1973 he joined the medical staff at St. Mary's. According to Johnson, "...we have outstanding anesthetists and the best intensive-care nurses I have ever worked with." Numerous cardiac surgeons and cardiologists joined the staff, and pioneering methods and treatments were utilized. What began as a program for low-risk patients evolved into one of the top programs in the country treating patients from around the world.

However, even the development of these specialized departments and the resulting growth of staff did not detract from the ongoing commitment at St. Mary's to serve the general medical needs of the community that was its home.

Meeting Community Needs

Sister Priscilla Grimes, who came to St. Mary's during the early 1970s and was hospital administrator between 1976 and 1981, recalled the many ways

125TH ANNIVERSARY ST. MARY'S HOSPITAL

Sister Julianna Kelly, hospital administrator from 1966 to 1978, looks west from St. Mary's Seton Hall at the foundation being laid for Seton Tower, the Todd Wehr Diagnostic Center, and the future patient care tower. Started in 1973, the buildings were completed in 1976.

Sister Priscilla Grimes watched history in the making as St. Mary's grew with the city it served. Before she became hospital administrator in 1978, Sister Priscilla witnessed the start of the heart program and the expansion of the burn center—two programs that remain prominent today.

in which the hospital leadership and staff worked to meet the community's ever-changing needs. While she was at St. Mary's, the burn unit was expanded because of increasing demand for its specialized services. Many patients were flown in from both civilian and military accidents, including crash victims from Air Force Reserve units. The burn unit had become St. Mary's hallmark, placing the hospital on the map for its outstanding specialization and success rate.

It was also during her tenure that St. Mary's worked closely with the Milwaukee Blue Cross office to develop the area's first smoothly functioning health maintenance organization, called the "Northpoint HMO." Through this plan, patients would be assisted in obtaining preventive medical care as well as emergency services through a joint agreement between Blue Cross, physicians, and the hospital. It became a model plan, upon which many later HMOs across the state were based.

As administrator, Grimes also recalled what a great drawing place the water tower just south of the hospital was during that "hippie time." The young crowd of the 1970s often turned to drugs and, as a result, created a need for a rehabilitation program. In response, St. Mary's opened a free clinic in the basement of the former school of nursing with a volunteer staff. This service to all segments of the population was true to the original mission of the sisters 125 years before, when they established whatever programs they could to meet the ever-changing needs of the Milwaukee community, from caring for the indigent, the diseased, and the homeless

Below and facing: *On September 20, 1964, the Daughters of Charity around the world modernized their style of habit by replacing the familiar cornette with a simple blue coiffe with white lining. (The cornette, made of linen and soaked in heavy starch, was dried and then folded into its unique winged shape.) Ten years later the Daughters of Charity would modify the headdress yet again, this time minimizing the white lining.*

to serving orphans and the elderly.

In an effort to serve the homebound elderly in the 1970s, St. Mary's became a part of the "Meals on Wheels" program, whereby volunteer drivers would take nutritious hot meals from the institution's kitchen and deliver them to the elderly who were having difficulty shopping or cooking meals for themselves. The hospital also began a home care program for shut-ins during this decade. In a similar fashion, St. Mary's responded to a new need in the field of medical internships.

During the early 1970s many physicians realized that the emphasis on preventive health care meant they could serve entire families, thereby eliminating the need for repetitive trips to many different doctors. It was often easier to treat communicable diseases, however slight or serious, if the same physician saw all of the members of the same family. The new specialty was labeled "family practice" and became a prominent branch of internal medicine.

In July 1974 the Family Practice Clinic, jointly sponsored by St. Mary's Hospital and the University of Wisconsin-Madison, opened its doors. It was the state's first cooperative venture between a private hospital and a state-supported medical institution for training family practice doctors. The clinic later affiliated with the Medical College of Wisconsin. Like the Obstetrics and Gynecology Clinic, Family Practice offered quality medical treatment through a program staffed by residents under the supervision of competent specialists.

Facilities for the Future

By 1975 construction was under way for Seton Tower, the Todd Wehr Diagnostic Center, and the patient care tower, now known as the west facility. It was a massive new building program, the largest in the hospital's 125-year history. The fund raising required for these three new additions topped the $2-million mark.

Moreover, in addition to the three new buildings, St. Mary's agreed to take over the operation of the old St. Mary's Hill Hospital, a psychiatric facility that had been established in 1912 by another sisterhood, the School Sisters of St. Francis, but was in need of a strong institutional partner. This residential psychiatric facility

Hospital administrator Sister Julianna Kelly, Archbishop William E. Cousins (second from left), and other hospital representatives break ground for the new facility—located just across Lake Drive from the 1909 hospital building. Immediately following the ceremony, local dignitaries, employees, and neighborhood residents attended a reception hosted by hospital employees.

moved into the hospital's north wing in 1976, occupying space left when other programs relocated to the tower or the Wehr Center across the street. An underground tunnel had been constructed to connect all of the buildings and allow for the smooth transfer of patients and staff from one area to another.

Across the country, the growing awareness of those suffering from mental health problems and the potential for new drug treatments was coming to the forefront of hospitals' attention. From its beginning St. Mary's had provided care for the mentally ill, although very little was known about how to treat, much less control or cure, this disease in the nineteenth and early twentieth centuries. By the 1970s specialists in the field of psychiatry had benefited from the extensive research being done in the field of biochemistry. Adding the staff and background of St. Mary's Hill Hospital, long a distinct program, to its facility brought this new field of psychiatric medicine into the St. Mary's fold.

One Hundred and Twenty-Five Years and Growing

The hospital had marked its 125th anniversary in 1973, during an era when American society was caught in the turmoil at the end of the Vietnam War. Returning veterans brought new challenges to hospitals and new dilemmas to the field of psychiatry, as doctors struggled to deal with the many post-battlefield syndromes the war had created. The 1970s also brought an upsurge in the popularity of the field of nursing, and although St. Mary's nursing program remained closed, the growing number of nursing candidates brought many fresh faces to the hospital wards as in-house training at St. Mary's remained a highly desirable choice for students in the program at nearby UW-Milwaukee.

The next 25 years would bring dramatic changes to the health care field, and St. Mary's would face the multiple challenges of nursing shortages, rising insurance costs, and the growth of large interstate, for-profit hospital corporations.

Inventiveness to Infinity

1976–1998

ity to the patient care tower. The entire move took less than three hours. With the addition of the tower portion of the hospital, St. Mary's entered the era of hospital high-rises.

The new Todd Wehr Diagnostic Center at St. Mary's provided virtually every medical service on its 14-acre campus. St. Mary's was the most highly utilized hospital in the Milwaukee area, with a continuing occupancy rate that hovered around 90 percent, a figure that stood at the top of the national average for hospitals as well, according to a study done by the Commission on Hospital Care.

A S THE 1970S DAWNED, private hospitals across the country struggled to blend their mission of service with new challenges in the business climate. The decades of the 1970s, 1980s, and 1990s brought rising insurance costs, competition from large interstate hospital corporations, and a continuing need to balance staffing needs and salaries with tight budgets. Private hospitals also had to walk a fine line between the per diem charges for patients, the new federal programs of Medicare and Medicaid, and their ongoing need to engage in fund raising. St. Mary's loyal supporters continued their philanthropy to allow the hospital to grow and to meet these many new challenges.

The West Facility

Unlike the big move 67 years before, the opening of the west facility on Memorial Day weekend in 1976 required more than wheelbarrows. The National Guard, along with volunteers and hospital personnel, moved 165 patients and their room furnishings through the old tunnel in the east facil-

A Hospice, a Home

With the increasing incidence of cancer and its growing mortality rate, the hospital perceived another urgent need, the need for a place that would allow the terminally ill to die with dignity. Oncology patients, who reached a stage where their cancer was incurable, often desired a facility where their physical need for pain control could be met, as well as their need for basic nursing care. This need was not one that reached for recovery, but rather one that sought a humane death. These new facilities, which came to be called "hospices," provided skilled nursing care and sensitivity to both the patient's and family's needs in a time of great sorrow and stress.

St. Mary's Hospice, one of the first in-patient hospice programs in the state, was opened on November 3, 1980. It was designed to serve not only terminal patients, but their friends and family as well, in a quiet and hospitable surrounding where counseling was also available. The gentleness of the hospice program, in situations where hope for recovery was minimal or nonexistent, was reminiscent of the care provided a century earlier by the

Right: *St. Mary's Cancer Center—a part of the hospital since 1981—is supported by various programs including medical oncology, gynecological oncology, radiation oncology, surgical oncology, hospice care, and research. The center maintains a cancer registry, a data base of patients diagnosed or treated for cancer at St. Mary's since 1985, and is noted for offering the area's first ongoing ovarian cancer screening program for women at high risk.*

Below: *The Daughters of Charity maintained a strong presence in young girls' lives at St. Rose Orphanage for 129 years. By 1977 the last two Daughters at St. Rose were reassigned to places with a greater need. Today St. Rose Residence carries on the Daughters' tradition, providing love, care, and guidance to help young girls develop into caring women. Courtesy, St. Rose Residence*

first sisters at St. Mary's when they tended those dying of smallpox or cholera. Nurturing and pain reduction in a sanitary environment was the hallmark in the terminal wards of both the 1850s and the 1980s.

St. Mary's Hospice provided for more than 200 people in its first 10 years of operation. In the words of the Reverend James Fisher, who spoke at the facility's dedication: "Hospice is people, people with skills, people who care, people who affirm love, and people endowed with the raw courage to hold the hand of another at the very edge of life."

Other New Services

The hospice was only one of the many new ways in which St. Mary's found itself creating programs to serve emerging community needs. The hospital developed many new services in its obstetrics department to better serve women with high-risk pregnancies and to reduce the rate of infant mortality. Many babies born at St. Mary's might not have survived without the gamete intra-fallopian transfer program, the perinatal screening program, or the Neonatal Intensive Care Unit. In September 1997 the Arnold quintuplets were born

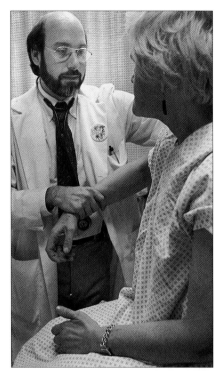

at St. Mary's, the second set of surviving quintuplets ever born in Wisconsin. What once was unimaginable had become possible, though no less miraculous. Along with better care for mothers and babies, the hospital was increasingly aware of the need to serve both its neighborhood and its own staff with a daycare program. With the increasing number of nurses who were married and had children, part of attracting a top-rated staff depended upon the availability of high-quality child care.

Seton Children's School

The answer to these problems was designed so that the neighborhood near the hospital—as well as the hospital's staff—could benefit from child care availability. The Seton Children's School, at St. Hedwig's Parish on Brady Street, opened on August 26, 1981. By the end of its first decade, the Seton School—named after Mother Elizabeth Seton—had served 700 children at its original site, as well as at two additional locations.

Above: *In 1976 St. Mary's moved into what was called "Tomorrow's Hospital Today." The 300-bed acute care facility, housed in an eight-floor clover-leaf configuration, was designed to efficiently meet the needs of St. Mary's patients.*

Left: *Seton Children's School, which began offering day care services in 1981, has served many youngsters through the years. Today the school provides care to 450 infants and children from three locations—St. Mary's Milwaukee, St. Mary's Ozaukee, and in Foxpoint.*

St. Mary's Women's & Children's Center opened the hospital's first Perinatal Assessment Center in January 1994, becoming one of only two in Milwaukee to provide these specialized services. Barb Gesme (center), RN, PAC coordinator, discusses the new ultrasound equipment with Sister Patricia Huffman, D.C., and Sister Renée Rose, D.C., at the center's open house. The PAC provides consultations with a perinatologist, as well as testing and diagnosis services to patients in need of high-risk obstetric care.

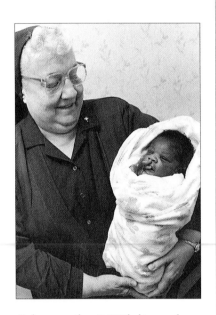

Today more than 2,000 babies are born each year at St. Mary's.

At the end of 1997 the Seton Children's School moved to a new location just one block from the hospital in a new building on the grounds of the Milwaukee Catholic Home, adjacent to the tower portion of the hospital.

Hospitals and the Space Age

From the space age, which began just before 1960, and from the Vietnam era of technological breakthroughs, came a dramatically different way to perform surgery, known as laser surgery. Using a laser, or a concentrated beam of high-intensity light rays, surgeons were able to make an entirely new kind of incision. The word "laser" was derived from its definition as "light amplification by stimulated emission of radiation," a concept originally proposed in 1917 by Albert Einstein. The first operating laser was created by American physicist Peter Sorokin in 1966, patented in 1977, and thereafter adapted for medical use.

The use of lasers in surgery began in the 1980s, and at St. Mary's in 1983. The process was attractive because it held several key advantages over traditional incisions with a scalpel. A laser was able to cut much more precisely without damaging surrounding tissue. It also caused less bleeding and required less anesthetic. Lasers could be used to remove a tumor, coagulate a blood vessel, remove a birthmark, or restore sight to a patient with cataracts.

In addition to lasers, there were other aspects of the space age that enhanced medical progress through the testing of drugs and chemical processes in the weightlessness beyond the earth's atmosphere.

The Genesis of Project JULIE

Not only was St. Mary's one of the earlier hospitals to develop laser capa-

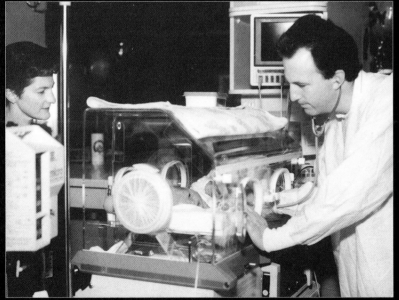

St. Mary's Neonatal Intensive Care Unit, which opened in 1990, provides care to the hospital's tiniest patients. The NICU, staffed by numerous specialists including neonatologists and neonatal nurse practitioners, is equipped to treat infants delivered at less than 26 weeks' gestation. NICU staff currently treat between 200 and 300 patients a year.

The second set of surviving quintuplets born in Wisconsin was delivered at St. Mary's in September 1997. Cared for in the NICU, the healthy infants went home just a few weeks after birth. Pictured (left to right) are the Arnold babies: Devin, Emily, Natalie, Alyssa, and Daniel. Photo by Jon Roob, W&J Roob Photography; courtesy, the Arnold family

NASA shuttles. Muckerheide called the project Joint Utilization of Laser Integrated Experiments—Project JULIE—after Sister Julie Hanser, then president of St. Mary's Hospital. In response to the honor of having St. Mary's become a national pioneering institution in this new frontier in space medicine, Sister Julie spoke of the "awesome" potential of the NASA program and of its "significant potential to expand the development of health care and...alleviate human suffering."

Project JULIE was made up of 20 experiments designed to study the effect of laser light, cosmic radiation, and weightlessness on medications, human tissues, laser protective eyewear, fiber optics, and other materials in space. Seven very small lasers were included in the payload, which weighed 80 pounds.

In response to the question about the value of medical research in space, Muckerheide responded, "There's no laboratory on earth that can simulate the days of microgravity that the shuttle affords." An experiment to study blood typing, which was normally dependent on gravity for clumping, was placed aboard the shuttle as part of Project JULIE. In addition, the project scientists studied the effect of lasers and cosmic radiation on medications used in the treatment of cancer.

"It is truly exciting," Sister Julie Hanser told the staff, "that a private hospital in Milwaukee, Wisconsin, can work with NASA, and...combine resources in a project like this." The project's dimensions were almost limitless, and its potential to expand medical knowledge provided an incredible opportunity. The partnership was

In February 1996 many of St. Mary's physicians were listed in a special "Top Docs" section of Milwaukee Magazine. *Three physicians who practiced at St. Mary's were featured inside and on the cover. Courtesy,* Milwaukee Magazine

bility, it also welcomed an exciting opportunity to enter the space age in another way. Early in 1983 Myron C. "Mike" Muckerheide, director of the Genesis Laser Laboratory at St. Mary's, was authorized by the National Aeronautics and Space Administration (NASA) to develop a laser project for space flight. St. Mary's was the first hospital—in the world—to be accepted and to participate in NASA's Get-Away Special (GAS) program.

The program was initiated to fly self-contained scientific payloads on seen as a testimony to the ability of St. Mary's to keep abreast of space age technology, so vastly removed from the stars over Milwaukee viewed by the earliest Sisters of Charity on their westward journey a century and a half earlier. The horizons of medical knowledge had expanded beyond their wildest dreams.

Liftoff and Landing

Project JULIE was launched aboard the space shuttle *Columbia* on January 12, 1986, and returned to earth six days later. Many individual laser scientists and physicians from around the United States also contributed to the project, which was funded by private donations. Upon the shuttle's return to earth, the payload that had traveled three million miles was donated to the National Air and Space Museum in Washington, D.C. A model of the shuttle was also put on display at the General Mitchell International Airport Gallery of Flight Aviation History Museum in Milwaukee. A number of inventions resulted from the Project JULIE experiments.

An Ongoing Commitment to Serve the Poor

The economic recession of the 1980s

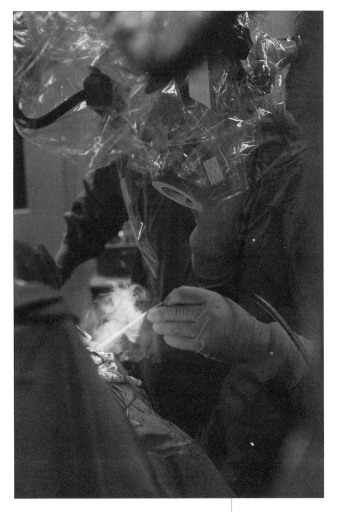

presented the hospital with more opportunities to serve the community. In its continuing effort to reach out to the city's most needy, St. Mary's Hospital agreed in 1988 to take over

In 1982 efforts were made to acquire equipment to perform laser surgery at St. Mary's and also to provide training in laser usage and safety. Under the guidance of Mike Muckerheide, director of the Laser Laboratory, five experienced surgical nurses at St. Mary's became the first class of registered nurses in the state to be certified in laser safety.

Mike Muckenheide was director of St. Mary's Genesis Laser Laboratory from 1983 to 1996, as well as laser safety officer. A director of Project JULIE, which was carried aboard the space shuttle Columbia, Muckerheide coordinated the efforts of 17 doctors and scientists from across the United States.

Right: *Residents of the Milwaukee Catholic Home, located just behind St. Mary's west facility, donated hand-knit baby clothing for hospital newborns in one of many efforts to work together as partners in the community.*

Below: *Josephine Alden volunteered as an "on call" interpreter for many St. Mary's patients over the years. She received a special commendation in 1991 by President George Bush when he awarded her a "Daily Point of Light" medal.*

responsibility for St. Ben's Clinic, after the closure of St. Anthony's Hospital at 27th and Wells streets. The clinic had provided free medical care to residents of one of Milwaukee's most troubled neighborhoods for many decades, but could no longer function unless it joined with a larger unit. Rather than have the neighborhood lose this vital program, St. Mary's agreed to take the clinic under its wing and keep it open. The spirit of St. Vincent de Paul and St. Louise de Marillac was alive and well in this decision, as was the initial inspiration of Bishop Henni, the hospital's founding father.

The hospital did not limit its embrace of these needy to the clinic. It also brought patients from this neighborhood into its main facility, when necessary, to provide a full range of hospital services, however specialized or costly. In 1988-1989 St. Mary's provided $800,000 worth of burn care and other emergency medical treatment for those with little or no health

Left: *St. Ben's Clinic, sponsored by St. Mary's since the late 1980s, provides health care services for Milwaukee-area homeless adults. The nurse-managed clinic operates with the support of volunteers including physicians, receptionists, and an office manager. This 1993 photo shows (left to right) nurses Molly Kluth and Carol Sejda standing with one of their many patients.*

Below left: *St. Mary's volunteers provide many services within the hospital, including weekly free blood pressure screenings. Their contributions to St. Mary's employees and patients are recognized each year at an annual Volunteer Recognition Awards Dinner.*

Below: *Hundreds of "baskets" like this one are filled each year during St. Mary's Thanksgiving Basket Donation, organized by the Community Services Department. Each basket— accompanied by a certificate for a turkey—is presented to families just before Thanksgiving Day.*

insurance. Support was also offered to the 16th Street Clinic, on Milwaukee's near south side, where residents received many of the same medical and nutrition programs.

Welcoming Strangers

By the late 1970s, 15 percent of the patients at St. Mary's were from foreign countries. As heart surgery wasn't available in Europe until the late 1980s, many cardiac patients came to Milwaukee. One heart patient commented about his reception, in 1992, when he arrived at the Milwaukee airport and hired a taxicab to drive him to St. Mary's. Immediately, the cab driver turned around to query his two passengers

Licheng Zhang, a native of China, became yet another patient from across the world who underwent heart surgery at St. Mary's. In 1992 Zhang experienced heart problems while visiting his daughter Susa, but was unable to afford the needed surgery. He underwent multiple bypass heart surgery with the help of the heart surgeon, cardiologists, and pulmonologist who donated their services, and St. Mary's Charity Care program. Zhang, thankful but unable to speak English, later presented the hospital with two hand-made calligraphy scrolls that translated to mean, "St. Mary's humanitarian efforts are shown in the care of the sick and needy."

Right: *St. Mary's Hill Hospital, built in 1912, was originally located on the corner of West Greenfield Avenue and South 32nd Street. In 1976 the hospital moved to Lake Drive (next to St. Mary's east facility and currently the site of Sacred Heart Rehabilitation Institute.) The Daughters of Charity became sponsors of St. Mary's Hill Hospital in 1991, providing inpatient and outpatient services for children, adolescents, and adults.*

about which one was headed to the hospital to "get his ticker fixed." The hospital's reputation as a premier cardiac care unit had reached across the city.

The influx of patients who couldn't speak English—an echo of the hospital's clientele during the nineteenth century—led to the formation of a translator's list. By the 1990s the list included the names of more than 50 people who spoke everything from Arabic to Russian. Charity cases from

as far away as China were treated at St. Mary's through a variety of organizations and donations. Funds for airfare for a patient and an accompanying family member were raised by a committee of sponsors. Physicians often donated a part of their fees to help serve these people in need, particularly children.

However, even this extensive altruism could not change the economic difficulties faced by many hospitals during the recession of the 1980s and the rising costs of health care in the 1990s. Even with a mission of service and charity, a hospital was still a business institution that had to heed its balance sheets in order to keep its doors open.

Changes in the Business of Medicine

Many of these economic challenges in the health care field were met through consolidation. St. Mary's acquired the assets of the Northpoint Medical Group in 1990, and became a full sponsor of St. Mary's Hill Hospital, a psychiatric care unit, in 1991. Numerous changes in health insurance took place during this time, among

them the formation of health maintenance organizations and a decrease in coverage for inpatient treatment. As a result of these changes, Comprehensive Counseling Services was formed within St. Mary's itself, and the old program at St. Mary's Hill Hospital finally had to be closed.

The movement toward consolidation of health care facilities continued throughout the 1990s. In 1994, after much evaluation, St. Mary's joined Horizon, a health care network started in 1989 that includes Columbia Hospital, Community Memorial Hospital Menomonee Falls, Froedert Memorial Lutheran Hospital, and Kenosha Hospital and Medical Center. Under the guidance of Sister Renée Rose, who became president and CEO

of St. Mary's in 1989 and today serves as CEO of Horizon Healthcare, St. Mary's entered into a joint operating agreement with Columbia Hospital.

With the acquisition of the Sacred Heart Rehabilitation Institute in 1995, St. Mary's Hospital was able to enhance its program of long- and short-term physical, occupational, and respiratory care and rehabilitation to people from all cultural and economic backgrounds. Another door of service was opened.

Throughout the 1980s and 1990s the complex nature of government funding programs brought the American Hospital Association and the Catholic Hospital Association into the halls of Congress many times to lobby on behalf of the welfare of hospitals across the country. Both groups strug-

In April 1984 the Flight for Life helicopter landed at St. Mary's for the first time, transporting a young burn patient from Tomahawk, Wisconsin. Flight for Life primarily transports burn patients and on occasion cardiac patients to St. Mary's for specialized care. A helipad, located just north of the patient tower, allows patients to be quickly and easily moved.

Below: *St. Mary's Hospital expanded into Ozaukee County in 1985 after purchasing the county's only hospital, St. Alphonsus, from the Sisters of the Sorrowful Mother. The facility, located in Port Washington, was renamed St. Mary's Hospital Ozaukee. Courtesy, St. Mary's Hospital Ozaukee*

gled to work with commissions studying the rising costs of hospital care and the implications for hospital size, charitable outreach efforts, and government subsidies for health care.

Private hospitals, like St. Mary's and others, with a long tradition of service to the community's most needy, have had to examine their roles in light of budget realities. The continuation of a tradition of such service has only been possible through the philanthropic efforts of both donors to the hospital and the hospital's ongoing commitment to continue such service.

On April 19, 1994, St. Mary's Hospital Ozaukee moved from Port Washington to its current location in Mequon. The new, 82-bed replacement facility was planned and designed with input from medical staff, community members, and employees. Courtesy, St. Mary's Hospital Ozaukee

St. Mary's Foundation

Through all of the budgetary challenges, St. Mary's has continued to provide affordable care to those in need. In 1978 the St. Mary's Foundation was created to increase fund development. By the 1990s the hospital was budgeting more than $2 million dollars a year for inpatient charity care and community programs. Typical projects funded by the foundation included building renovation, new technology and equipment, doctor and nurse education grants, hospice services, cancer center equipment, funding for infant programs, employee scholarships, and community outreach programs.

Celebrating 150 Years

St. Mary's Hospital celebrates its 150th anniversary in 1998, in a city far different than that of Milwaukee in 1848. While the world has changed dramatically, the central vision of the hospital has remained one of caring for the sick, no matter what their race, nationality, illness, or ability to pay. The shape of that dream was clear to Bishop John Martin Henni and the first three sisters who arrived in Milwaukee in 1846,

By the early 1990s the hospital's west facility was in need of a facelift in several areas and more space to meet the growing needs of outpatients. In 1992 construction began on a 61,000-square-foot addition and renovation of 37,000 square feet of existing space. The result included the addition of six new operating rooms, and a relocation of outpatient services, emergency department, GI lab, pre-admission and lab testing, and day surgery. The renovations included the addition of a new atrium connector walkway—still under construction in this photo.

Patients needing physical or occupational therapy and rehabilitation have access to services provided by St. Mary's Sports Medicine Center and Sacred Heart Rehabilitation Institute.

Mary Simeon Burns, Mary Ann Paul, and Mary Agnes Frances Flanley. Echoing the goals of the hospital's first three servants, Sister Julie Hanser, D.C., hospital administrator from 1982 to 1989, reflected on the steadiness of that vision:

The mission of St. Mary's Hospital [remains] the healing ministry of Jesus Christ in today's world.

From the windows of the hospital's new tower in 1998, the view looks out to the waters of Lake Michigan that first brought the Sisters of Charity to Milwaukee on their healing mission. The panorama

also looks south to the center of the city, where their first outpost of nursing, St. John's Infirmary, was established in the shadow of the cathedral whose spire still dominates the city's east side. The view from the hospital's windows today encompasses the entire city, the history of which would have been drastically different without St. Mary's healing presence throughout the past 150 years.

Below: *In 1995 St. Mary's entered into a joint operating agreement with neighboring Columbia Hospital to improve the scope and coordination of health care services to the Milwaukee and Ozaukee communities. Pictured are Sister Renée Rose, president and CEO of St. Mary's Hospital from 1989 to 1996, and John Schuler, former president and CEO of Columbia Health System. Today Sister Renée Rose serves as president and CEO of Horizon Healthcare, Inc., while John Schuler serves as president and CEO of the newly formed Columbia•St. Mary's, Inc.*

Epilogue

St. Mary's Current and Future Role

The delivery of health care continues to change based on new demands of patients and purchasers. Health care consumers and their families are becoming more involved in decision making and want easier access to high-quality services. The government, insurance companies, and employers (those who pay many of the bills) seek lower costs for services. Health care organizations are responding to these needs and pressures by linking together in innovative, new relationships.

While St. Mary's has always been part of a larger national system of hospitals (Daughters of Charity National Health System), it recently became important to consider local ties as well. In 1994 the board of directors and leadership of St. Mary's Milwaukee completed significant talks and evaluations with other health care providers in the Milwaukee area. Following this evaluation, the obvious choice was the Horizon Healthcare System. Horizon Healthcare was formed in 1989 by sponsoring members including Columbia Hospital, Community Memorial Hospital of Menomonee Falls, and Froedtert Memorial Lutheran Hospital. This group had much in common with the St. Mary's organizations in terms of a philosophy of partnership; shared mission and values; and long-standing histories as strong, community-based organizations.

Soon after joining Horizon, the leadership of St. Mary's Hospital and Columbia Hospital began talking about how they could better cooperate in serving overlapping parts of the Milwaukee community. In July 1995 the boards of both organizations approved a unique form of merger known as a Joint Operating Agreement. The new organization, known as Columbia•St. Mary's, includes Columbia Hospital, St. Mary's Hospital of Milwaukee, St. Mary's Hospital Ozaukee, Sacred Heart Rehabilitation Institute, and the Columbia•St. Mary's-Community Physicians. The "essence" of the Columbia•St. Mary's purpose is to be:

- a community serving community to improve people's health,

- the best at serving patients and supporting physicians,

- guided by the values of trust and respect; physicians as partners; quality; cost competitiveness; collaboration; and service for all in the community.

Through Columbia•St. Mary's, St. Mary's Hospital of Milwaukee and its partners will continue to share their gifts and abilities to meet the health care needs of Milwaukee area residents for the next 150 years.

Directors of St. Mary's School of Nursing

1894-1899	Sister Loretto Vaughn
1899-1902	Sister Lucia James
1903	Sister Blanche
1904-1910	Sister Vincent Kuhn
1911	Sister Christine
1912-1924	Sister Stephanie Wahl
1924-1932	Sister Anne O'Connor
1932-1938	Sister Emile Neidhammer
1938-1957	Sister Mercedes Harrison
1957-1961	Sister Austin Cusimano
1961-1969	Sister (Benigna) Lucille Beauchamp

Hospital Administrators

St. John's Infirmary

1848-1853	Sister Felicitas Delone
1853-1855	Sister Rose Doherty

St. Mary's Hospital

1855-1875	Sister Vincent McEntree
1875-1883	Sister Joseph Melody
1883-1892	Sister Julia Dyers
1892-1898	Sister Loretto Vaughn
1899-1902	Sister Lucia James
1903	Sister Felicite McNulty
1904-1927	Sister Dolores Gillespie
1927-1933	Sister Magdalen Welsh
1933-1941	Sister Alberta Sullivan
1942-1954	Sister Rose Maguire
1954-1960	Sister Hermine Regan
1960-1966	Sister Josephine Atchison
1966-1978	Sister Julianna Kelly
1978-1984	Sister Priscilla Grimes
1984-1989	Sister Julie Hanser
1989-1996	Sister Renée Rose
1996-Present	Charles Lobeck

Presidents of St. Mary's Hospital Medical Staff

1906-1910	James O'Brien, M.D.
1912-1914	James A. Bach, M.D.
1922-1926	W.C.F. Witte, M.D.
1927	E.W. Miller, M.D.
1928	Harry McCabe, M.D.
1929	Andrew J. Weber, M.D.
1930	Filip A. Forsbeck, M.D.
1931	Theodore H. Rolfs, M.D.
1932	A.F. Rheineck, M.D.
1933	Charles Fidler, M.D.
1934	T.A. Judge, M.D.
1935	Millard Tufts, M.D.
1936	G.V.I. Brown, M.D.
1937	Francis B. McMahon, M.D.
1938	Louis A. Fuerstenau, M.D.
1939	Theodore H. Burbach, M.D.
1940	Charles M. Schoen, M.D.
1941	C.J. Corcoran, M.D.
1942	Dexter H. Witte, M.D.
1943	John T. Klein, M.D.
1944	William M. Jermain, M.D.
1945	Peter E. Oberbreckling, M.D.
1946	S.R. Mitchell, M.D.
1947	Dexter H. Witte, M.D.
1948	John T. Klein, M.D.
1949	Edwin J. Bach, M.D.
1950	Ervin L. Bernhart, M.D.
1951	E.J. Schelble, M.D.
1952	A.D. Spooner, M.D.
1953	John Enright, M.D.
1954	Jerome Fons, M.D.
1955	E.L. Bernhart, M.D.
1956-1959	Dexter H. Witte, M.D.
1960-1961	Joseph A. Devitt, M.D.
1962-1965	M.C.F. Lindert, M.D.
1966-1970	David Ovitt, M.D.
1971-1973	Anthony J. Sanfelippo, M.D.
1973-1975	Thomas W. Grossman, M.D.
1975-1977	John A. Kelble, M.D.
1977-1980	David J. Carlson, M.D.
1980-1982	George Collentine, M.D.
1982-1984	William C. Fetherston, M.D.
1984-1986	H. James Hamm, M.D.
1986-1988	Thomas J. Cox, M.D.
1988-1990	Edward F. Banaszak, M.D.
1990-1992	Gordon Lang, M.D.
1992-1994	C.R. Raj, M.D.
1994-1996	Glenn Ragalie, M.D.
1996-Present	David Hoogerland, M.D.

Appendices

Bibliography

Barnes-Svarney, Patricia, ed. *New York Public Library Science Desk Reference*. New York: Macmillan, 1995.

Cartwright, Frederick F., and Michael D. Biddis. *Disease and History*. New York: Barnes and Noble Books, 1972.

Code, Joseph B. *Mother Elizabeth Ann Seton*. New York: Paulist Press, circa 1931.

Conzen, Kathleen Neils. *Immigrant Milwaukee 1836-1860: Accommodation and Community in a Frontier City*. Cambridge: Harvard University Press, 1976

Daughters of St. Paul. *Mother Seton: Wife, Mother, Educator, Foundress, Saint*. Boston: St. Paul Editions, 1975.

Delaney, John J. *Dictionary of Saints*. New York: Doubleday, 1980.

Flower, Frank A. *History of Milwaukee From Prehistoric Times to the Present Date*. Chicago: Western Publishing Company, 1881.

Frank, Louis Frederick. *The Medical History of Milwaukee 1834-1914*. Milwaukee: Germania Publishing, 1915.

Franks, Ray. *Meanwhile Back at the Ranch*. Amarillo, Texas: Ray Franks Ranch, 1996.

Gregory, John G. *History of Milwaukee, Wisconsin, Vol. I*. Chicago: S.J. Clarke Publishing Company, 1931.

Harris, Walter. *The History of Medicine in Wisconsin*. El Paso, Texas: Walter J. Harris, 1958.

Johnson, Peter Leo. *Daughters of Charity in Milwaukee 1846-1946*. Milwaukee: The Daughters of Charity, 1946.

Kalisch, Phillip A., and Beatrice J. Kalisch. *The Advance of American Nursing*. Boston: Little, Brown and Company, 1978.

Lloyd, Wyndham E.B. *A Hundred Years of Medicine*. New York: Humanities Press, 1936.

Luedtke, Eleanor. *Caritas Christi: The Daughters of Charity of St. Vincent de Paul*. Southfield, Michigan: Providence Hospital and Medical Centers, 1994.

McNamara, Jo Ann Kay. *Sisters in Arms: Catholic Nuns Through Two Millenia*. London: Harvard University Press, 1996.

The Milwaukee Journal

The Milwaukee News

The Milwaukee Sentinel

Numbers, Ronald L., and Judith Walzer Leavitt, eds. *Wisconsin Medicine: Historical Perspectives*. Madison: University of Wisconsin Press, 1981.

Rosenberg, Charles E. *The Care of Strangers: The Rise of America's Hospital System*. New York: Basic Books, Inc., 1987.

Rummel, Leo. *History of the Catholic Church in Wisconsin*. Madison: Knights of Columbus, 1976.

St. Mary's Hospital Archives, University of Wisconsin, Area Research Center, Milwaukee, Wisconsin.

Smith, Alice E. *The History of Wisconsin, Vol. I: From Exploration to Statehood*. Madison: State Historical Society of Wisconsin, 1973.

Stepsis, Ursula, and Dolores Liptak, eds. *Pioneer Healers*. New York: Crossroad, 1989.

Still, Baird. *Milwaukee, The History of a City*. Madison: State Historical Society of Wisconsin, 1948.

Index